WORLDWATCH REPORT 181

Global Environmental Change: The Threat to Human Health

SAMUEL S. MYERS, MD, MPH

LISA MASTNY AND ROBERT ENGELMAN, *EDITORS*

WORLDWATCH INSTITUTE, WASHINGTON, DC

On the cover: A young girl in Gujarat, India, squats to get water from a hose hooked up to a pipeline that passes by the edge of her village.

Photograph © 2003 Shezeen Suleman, courtesy of Photoshare

Mixed Sources
Product group from well-managed forests, controlled sources and recycled wood or fiber
www.fsc.org Cert no. SW-COC-002062
© 1996 Forest Stewardship Council

Suggested citation: Samuel S. Myers, *Global Environmental Change: The Threat to Human Health*, Worldwatch Report 181 (Washington, DC: Worldwatch Institute, 2009).

Table of Contents

Figures, Tables, and Sidebars

Acknowledgments

This report is adapted with permission from an article by Samuel S. Myers and Jonathan A. Patz in Volume 34 of the *Annual Review of Environment and Resources*. The Worldwatch Institute thanks the editors of the journal for permission to publish parts of this paper in significantly revised form. The author thanks Paul Ehrlich, Rosamond Naylor, David Lobell, and Gretchen Daily at Stanford University, James McCarthy and Daniel Schrag at Harvard University, Felicia Keesing at Bard University, Richard Ostfeld at the Cary Institute of Ecosystem Studies, Kristie Ebi at ESS, LLC, and Timothy Wirth at the United Nations Foundation for helpful comments on an earlier draft of this manuscript. He also thanks Mary Sternitzky of the University of Wisconsin's Center for Sustainability and the Global Environment for help creating the figures. The editors thank Worldwatch intern Brenda Voloshin for editorial, research, and graphical assistance.

About the Author

Samuel S. Myers, MD, MPH is an Instructor of Medicine at Harvard Medical School and a Research Fellow at the Harvard University Center for the Environment. He practices and teaches internal medicine and serves as staff physician at Mount Auburn Hospital in Cambridge, MA. Dr. Myers is currently developing research into the health consequences of altered nutrient composition of crops in response to high concentrations of atmospheric carbon dioxide. In addition to teaching clinical medicine, he teaches courses about the health impacts of large-scale anthropogenic environmental change at Harvard University. In the past year, Dr. Myers has been lead author of an article for the *Annual Review of Environment and Resources* on "Emerging Threats to Human Health from Global Environmental Change" and has written several book chapters on the human health impacts of different types of large-scale environmental change, including land use change, climate change, and ecosystem service disruption. Dr. Myers has also worked for the U.S. Agency for International Development and Conservation International and lived for two years in a village in Tibet, China, where he was field manager for an integrated conservation and development project focusing on population, health, and the environment. A graduate of Harvard College, Dr. Myers received his MD from Yale University School of Medicine and his MPH from Harvard School of Public Health. He serves on the board of directors of the Worldwatch Institute.

Preface

The changes that human activities are causing to the Earth's basic physical and biological systems have always been much more than an environmental issue. But the world is only slowly waking up to the reality that environmental change threatens human health on an unprecedented scale—and in ways for which we are unprepared. Indeed, climate change combined with other types of large-scale, human-caused environmental change is increasingly recognized as one of the greatest public health challenges we have ever faced.

Human health and the health of the environment are intimately connected. Both are necessary to satisfy basic human needs. The environment is a key factor in determining the health of people. At the same time, investments in human health can help improve the health of the environment and ecological systems.

Both human health and the environment are under greater pressure than ever before. Up to one-third of the 25,000 child deaths that occur every day are due to dangers present in the environments where children live. Environment-related illnesses kill the equivalent of a jumbo-jet full of children every 30 minutes. This is a tragedy of immense dimensions, yet there is far less focus on the problem than it deserves. And it is the poor who bear the main burden.

While the challenges are greater than ever, we now have the ability more than ever before to secure good health for every individual and community. In this report, Dr. Myers emphasizes that most of the emerging health threats associated with large-scale environmental change are preventable. As such, the report is a call to action.

The knowledge that we *can* make a difference means that we have a large responsibility to act. By fighting ignorance, inaction, and inequity, we can create the conditions under which health threats can be averted. Most importantly, we must take targeted collective action to reduce the vulnerability of the poorest people on the planet to threats they played little role in generating.

Mitigation and adaptation are the two key strategies we need to follow. First, we must reduce emissions of greenhouse gases to a minimum in order to limit climatic disruption. A more stable climate will reduce vulnerability to the emerging threats that Dr. Myers highlights in this report: the spread of infectious diseases, increasing scarcity of food and uncontaminated fresh water, natural disasters, and widespread population displacement.

Second, we must help the poorest countries adapt to the consequences of environmental change. We must improve capacity to deal with the major emerging health threats on which this report focuses. Health systems and the economies that support them must be strengthened to withstand natural disasters and to detect and respond to changes in the distribution of infectious diseases. At the same time, we must broaden our focus beyond the traditional health sector to evaluate, and plan for, widespread changes in access to fresh water, agricultural production, and migration.

We must build capacity, at the national level, to perform risk assessments to identify the most important regional threats and develop interventions to reduce vulnerability to them. In addition to these specific efforts at adaptation, we will need to bolster general support for socially and environmentally sustainable growth. As living standards rise, people will be less likely to be swept aside by the next extreme weather event, epidemic, or crop failure.

More than two decades ago, I had the honor to chair the World Commission on Environment and Development. *Our Common Future*, the Commission's report released in 1987, helped introduce the concept of sustainable development into the vocabulary of the global debate. It is thus with great pleasure that I join the Worldwatch Institute and the United Nations Foundation in helping to launch the publication of this report. I hope it will be widely distributed, closely read, and quickly heeded by climate negotiators, governments, and the people they represent.

The report comes on the eve of the 15th Conference of the Parties to the United Nations Framework Convention on Climate Change, to be held in Copenhagen, Denmark. The health of the world, and particularly of the poor, hangs in the balance as we seek a global agreement to halt the human-caused alteration of our planet's climate. Human activity must be brought into balance with the Earth, on which our development and wellbeing ultimately depends.

—*Gro Harlem Brundtland,*
Special Envoy on Climate Change to United Nations Secretary-General Ban Ki-moon;
Director-General Emeritus,
World Health Organization;
former Prime Minister, Norway

Summary

Over the past two-to-three hundred years, humanity's ecological footprint has ballooned to such an extent that we are now fundamentally altering the planet. We have transformed the Earth's land surface and altered the function of its ecosystems, and we are triggering the rapid loss of both terrestrial and marine life. We are also profoundly changing our planet's climate. It is increasingly apparent that the breadth and depth of the changes we are wreaking on the environment are imperiling not only many of the other species with which we share the ecological stage, but the health and wellbeing of our own species as well.

Global climate change threatens human health in numerous and profound ways. Large segments of the population will experience more heat waves, altered exposure to infectious disease, and more-frequent natural disasters. Most significantly, climatic disruption threatens the adequacy of the core "building blocks" of health for large populations around the globe: sufficient food and nutrition, safe water for drinking and sanitation, fresh air to breathe, and secure homes to live in. As climate change dismantles these central elements of healthy societies, people with fewer resources will be forced to migrate in large numbers to lands where they may not be welcome. A likely result of all of these processes will be increased civic instability and strife.

Even if the global climate were stable, humans would still be converting more land, water, and ecosystem services for their own use. The environmental changes from these activities are combining to magnify several public health threats to the extent that they now endanger health and wellbeing globally and on scales never experienced in human history. These threats include: exposure to infectious disease, air pollution, water scarcity, food scarcity, natural disasters, and population displacement. Taken together, they represent the greatest public health challenge of the 21st century. We need to wake up to the danger and act with urgency to reduce ecological disruption as much as possible while simultaneously strengthening the resilience of populations to withstand the impacts of unavoidable environmental change.

Populations vary dramatically in their vulnerabilities to these emerging health threats, in part because the environmental changes that are triggering these threats are not uniform. Rapid glacial melting on the Tibetan plateau threatens the dry-season water supply for more than 1 billion people living and growing irrigated crops in Asia's great river basins. In sub-Saharan Africa, droughts and increased temperatures caused by climate change will interact with existing soil degradation, nutrient loss, and water scarcity to further reduce crop yields and constrain food supplies. The triple threat of more-severe storms, rising sea levels, and degraded coastal barriers—such as mangrove forests, coral reefs, wetlands, vegetated dunes, and barrier islands—will pose significant risks to low-lying coastal populations.

But vulnerability is not determined only by a population's exposure to health threats; it is also determined by the ability to adapt in the face of such threats. Many of the threats associated with global environmental change can be mitigated by means of trade, technology, infrastructure, behavior change, philanthropy, and governance. Populations with the resources—both economic and socio-cultural—to engage these mechanisms will suffer less than those without such resources. As a consequence, climate change threatens to further accentuate the divide between rich and poor, both across nations and within them.

Because the impacts will depend in large part on a population's location and socioeconomic status, it is critical that all countries conduct rigorous, location-specific risk assessments to identify which populations are at highest risk for which threats. Governments and other stakeholders will also need to mobilize substantial financial resources, technical capacity (both in assessment and appropriate technologies), and new partnerships that can help build capacity over the long term.

The health impacts of climate change present an opportunity as well as a challenge. The international community increasingly recognizes the moral imperative to help the poor reduce their vulnerability to climate change—a threat that developing countries have had little role in generating. At the same time, there is renewed emphasis on achieving the United Nations' Millennium Development Goals, as well as increasing attention in the United States to reforming foreign assistance. In this context, climate change may help to shine a light on some of the most entrenched challenges to human health in the poorest countries—including poverty, malnutrition, and infectious disease.

For many years, the industrialized world has done less than it could to relieve suffering among the global poor. Now, it will need to vigorously reframe its development assistance to address the impacts of climatic disruption—impacts for which it is largely responsible. With the upcoming climate talks in Copenhagen, Denmark, the year 2009 may be a defining moment in human history: a year in which the historical injustice of human-induced climate change could fuel an international effort to reduce vulnerability and simultaneously address some of the longest-standing scourges to human health.

Our challenge, for the rest of this century and beyond, will be to work to mitigate environmental change (for example, by reducing greenhouse gas emissions) and to increase the resilience of populations to the impacts of any changes that we are unable to mitigate (such as sea-level rise triggered by past emissions). Neither task should detract from the other; we must pursue both simultaneously and with equal fervor and strategic creativity. Along the way, there will be substantial opportunities to identify co-benefits, whereby a single intervention can both mitigate environmental threats and improve human health.

Addressing the health impacts of global environmental change needs to be a priority for the public health community, environmental scientists, and natural resource managers, as well as for governments and intergovernmental bodies such as the United Nations and multilateral development banks. What we need most are political will and financial resources. While these resources will need to be large, they are small compared to the cost of ignoring the impacts of large-scale change and trying to address the overwhelming problems of famine, epidemic disease, massive population displacement, and civil strife that may ensue.

Expanding the Focus of Environmental Health

As a species, we humans have been remarkably effective at rearranging the natural world to meet our own needs. This transformation has allowed for both rapid population growth and rapid economic development over the last few centuries—particularly over the last 50 years.[*][1] (See Figures 1 and 2.) These trends, in turn, have placed accelerating demands on the ecological goods and services that make our lives possible.

The result is that the entire ecosphere—oceans, land surface, atmosphere, and freshwater systems—has been modified extensively by human activities. For example:

- We now appropriate one-third to one-half of global ecosystem production for human consumption.[2]
- More than half of the nitrogen cycle is now driven by human activities.[3]
- We have converted roughly 40 percent of the Earth's ice-free land surface to cropland or pasture.[4]
- We use roughly half of the planet's accessible surface fresh water.[5]
- Over the past 300 years, we have reduced total forest cover by between 7 and 11 million square kilometers—an area the size of the continental United States.[†][6]
- Three-quarters of monitored fisheries are being fished at or beyond their sustainable limits.[7]
- To harness electricity, control flooding, and impound fresh water, we have built more

---

[*] Endnotes are grouped by section and begin on page 38.

[†] Units of measure throughout this report are metric unless common usage dictates otherwise.

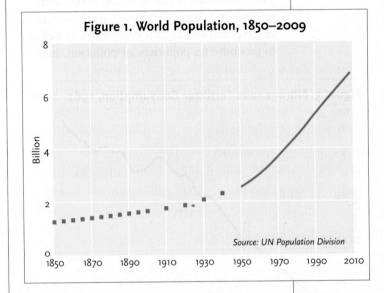

Figure 1. World Population, 1850–2009

Billion

Source: UN Population Division

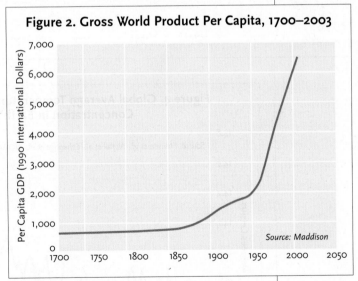

Figure 2. Gross World Product Per Capita, 1700–2003

Per Capita GDP (1990 International Dollars)

Source: Maddison

than 45,000 large dams and some 800,000 smaller dams around the world, altering the natural flow on roughly 60 percent of the world's rivers.[8]

- As a result of habitat loss, invasive species,

pollution, and climate change, we are driving species extinct at roughly 1,000 times the natural rate.[9]

Humans have also changed the planet's chemistry. We have altered global nutrient cycles by applying synthetic fertilizer to soil, much of which finds its way into nearby water bodies and the oceans.[10] (See Figure 3.) We now add more fixed nitrogen to the biosphere annually than all natural sources combined. These additions of nitrogen lead to biodiversity loss and changes in species compositions in terrestrial and aquatic ecosystems, as well as to groundwater pollution, air pollution, and acidification of soils and fresh water.[11] As a byproduct of our energy consumption and land use, we have increased the carbon dioxide (CO_2) in the atmosphere by roughly 30 percent over preindustrial levels, warming the planet artificially and making the oceans more acidic.[12] (See Figure 4.)

Despite historical concerns that population growth and increasing resource consumption might cause humanity to outstrip its ecological base, there has been little evidence at a global scale of a Malthusian collapse. To the contrary, from a human health perspective, our transformation of the planet appears to have been largely a success. Since 1820, average per capita income has risen eightfold.[13] In the year 1000, the average infant could expect to live about 24 years; today, she can expect to survive 66 years.[14] Infant and maternal mortality have fallen steeply, and per capita food production has risen despite a more-than fivefold increase in human population since 1820.[15]

These global averages hide dramatic disparities between rich and poor, and there remain large segments of the human population whose lives are curtailed by poverty, hunger, and disease. Nonetheless, by recruiting an ever larger share of the biosphere to meet human needs for food, water, fiber, building materials, and so on, a rapidly growing human population has largely prospered.

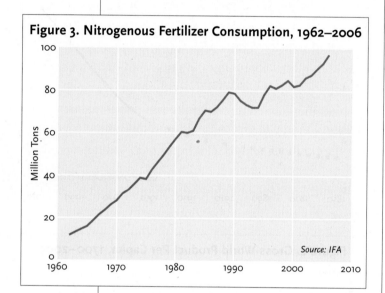

Figure 3. Nitrogenous Fertilizer Consumption, 1962–2006

Source: IFA

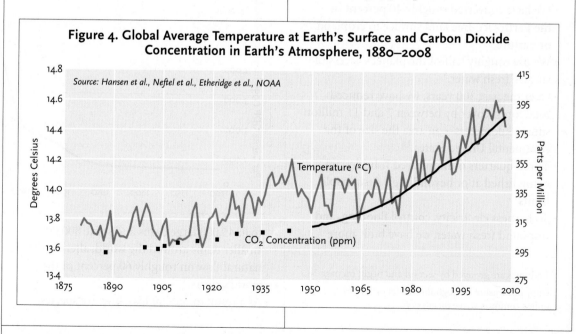

Figure 4. Global Average Temperature at Earth's Surface and Carbon Dioxide Concentration in Earth's Atmosphere, 1880–2008

Source: Hansen et al., Neftel et al., Etheridge et al., NOAA

Temperature (ºC)

CO_2 Concentration (ppm)

Yet at the same time, we have begun to identify emerging threats to human health that are deeply troubling. Accelerating changes to the Earth's climate, terrestrial surface, and ecosystems threaten our future access to some of the most basic components of public health: adequate nutrition, safe water, clean air, and protection from infectious disease and natural disasters. As access to these "building blocks" of health becomes more constrained, the health consequences for billions of people could be far reaching.

These changes justify a broadening of the concept of environmental health. Traditionally, this field has focused on analyzing the risks to humans associated with exposures to air and water pollution and to environmental toxins, such as heavy metals, radiation, and chemicals that mimic hormones or disrupt their balance in the body. With more than 100,000 manufactured chemicals now pervading the Earth's land, water, and soil—many of which are nearly ubiquitous in human bodies—policy change in this area is critical. But we also need to consider the broader health implications of the human transformation of the natural world.

Expanding the focus of environmental health would bring greater awareness to the major threats associated with large-scale, human-caused changes to the natural environment. Specifically, changes in land use, climate, and the function of ecosystems act synergistically to alter exposure to infectious disease and natural disasters, while curtailing access to food, clean air, and clean water and increasing the likelihood of population displacement and civil strife.

The broader health impacts of environmental change are difficult to study using traditional approaches because they are complex, caused by multiple factors, and often occur over very large scales. The effects are sometimes delayed significantly in time, and the momentum of past forces and alterations often

A desiccated animal carcass in northern Kenya is a symptom of the long-term drought there.

© 2006 Felix Masi/Voiceless Chilren, courtesy Photoshare

remains powerfully influential in the present. However, collaborative research into these relationships is gaining momentum by drawing on a variety of disciplines, utilizing new tools and methods, and developing innovative approaches to determining causality.[16]

Increasingly, some professional scientific societies are emphasizing the need for cooperative thinking across a range of natural, medical, and other social disciplines. These hybrid specialties go by such names as "eco-health," "conservation medicine," and the concept of "one health," whereby healthy people, wildlife, and environments are considered parts of a whole. Regardless of the terminology, it is clear that a new framework is needed for conceptualizing the connections between global environmental change and human health.

A New Health and Environment Framework

Humanity relies on the natural world to provide many of the cornerstones of health: adequate nutrition, clean water, clean air, and protection from infectious disease and natural disasters. Unfortunately, the combination of rapid land use change and accelerating climate disruption is reducing the capacity of ecosystems to continue providing these and other "services" at their historic capacities, and rates of depletion are accelerating.[1]

As ecosystem services degrade or become less available, human health is likely to suffer.[2] This seems intuitive, yet most studies exploring this association have underestimated the complexity of the relationship, with some finding no immediate correlation between the loss of ecosystem services and adverse health outcomes.[3] One reason for this conclusion is that most of us have the luxury of being blissfully unaware of how much we rely on the services that nature provides, since we tend to be insulated from the direct impacts of ecosystem service degradation by a variety of mitigating factors, from regional or international markets to effective infrastructure and governance.[4] (See Figure 5.)

Most societies rapidly externalize their "ecological footprint" beyond the local ecosystems where they live, making it hard to measure a direct correlation between ecological disruption and negative health outcomes. People who have access to regional or international markets can generally procure the food, fuel, fiber, and building materials they need. Most of us even buy water this way—in the form of the water required to produce imported grain, meat, or other food products. In this way, we insulate ourselves from the effects of local resource scarcity.[5] In contrast, people with little or no access to wider markets—particularly for food—are especially vulnerable to ecological degradation.[6]

A second reason that studies may miss important correlations between ecosystem degradation and adverse health is that other social, political, and economic factors—such as infrastructure and technology—can protect populations from the consequences of resource depletion.[7] The loss of wetlands and their water-filtering capacity, for example, is less likely to cause disease among downstream populations that have access to water-filtration technology. Meanwhile, the loss of coastal barriers such as mangroves, coral reefs, or vegetated dunes can increase vulnerability to extreme storms among residents who cannot afford to build sea walls and whose housing cannot withstand high winds or storm surges.

Behaviors learned from family members and the broader culture can also protect people from ecosystem change. Communities threatened by increased exposure to infectious disease as a result of altered environmental conditions may reduce their vulnerability through behaviors such as treating their drinking water, preparing foods in protective ways, or reducing exposure to disease-transmitting organisms by wearing protective clothing, using bed nets and screening, and staying indoors during certain hours. Because culturally determined behaviors often evolve over many generations and resist change, however, they may be less adaptable to rapidly changing environmental conditions.

Governance is another mediating factor. A

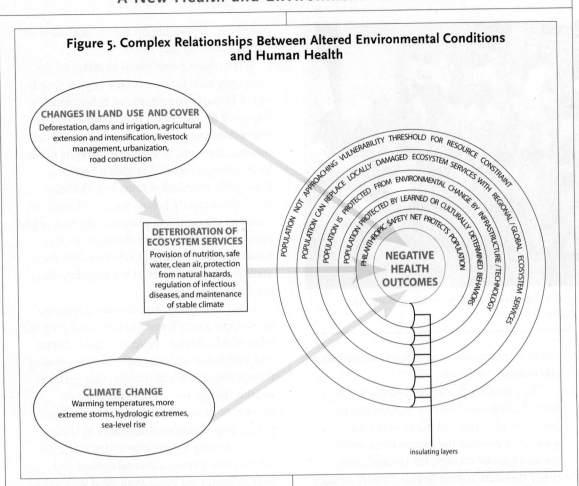

Figure 5. Complex Relationships Between Altered Environmental Conditions and Human Health

CHANGES IN LAND USE AND COVER
Deforestation, dams and irrigation, agricultural extension and intensification, livestock management, urbanization, road construction

DETERIORATION OF ECOSYSTEM SERVICES
Provision of nutrition, safe water, clean air, protection from natural hazards, regulation of infectious diseases, and maintenance of stable climate

CLIMATE CHANGE
Warming temperatures, more extreme storms, hydrologic extremes, sea-level rise

POPULATION NOT APPROACHING VULNERABILITY THRESHOLD FOR RESOURCE CONSTRAINT

POPULATION CAN REPLACE LOCALLY DAMAGED ECOSYSTEM SERVICES WITH REGIONAL/GLOBAL ECOSYSTEM SERVICES

POPULATION IS PROTECTED FROM ENVIRONMENTAL CHANGE BY INFRASTRUCTURE/TECHNOLOGY

POPULATION PROTECTED BY LEARNED OR CULTURALLY DETERMINED BEHAVIORS

PHILANTHROPIC SAFETY NET PROTECTS POPULATION

NEGATIVE HEALTH OUTCOMES

insulating layers

government's capacity and commitment to deliver resources such as food, water, and energy can prevent local resource scarcity from causing human suffering. Most of the famines of the 20th century, for example, were driven more by failures of governance and resource distribution than by absolute food scarcity.[8] International philanthropy may be the final safety net in settings where there is no access to international markets and where governance has failed, yet even access to philanthropic efforts varies widely by location and can be stymied by unreceptive governments, as was seen in Myanmar immediately following Typhoon Nargis in 2008.

The relationship between resource scarcity and health outcomes is likely linear only to a certain point.[9] (See Figure 6.) When resources such as food or clean water are limited, increases in access to them can bring significant health improvements. But once people have adequate access to these resources, the

relationship between increased access and health gains becomes much less pronounced. Further increases in access may lead to marginal improvements in health status, but overuse of resources may lead to reduced

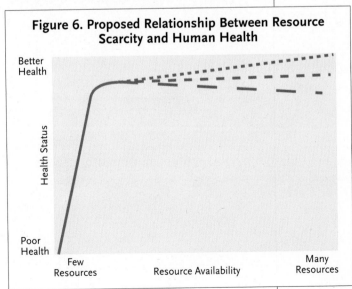

Figure 6. Proposed Relationship Between Resource Scarcity and Human Health

Better Health

Poor Health

Health Status

Few Resources

Resource Availability

Many Resources

Courtesy USAID

Milk distribution at a therapeutic feeding center in Kalonge, Democratic Republic of Congo.

health status, as with excess food consumption and obesity.

The causal chain between global environmental change and health impacts can be quite complex and can occur over long time scales that obscure the connections. Both land use and climate change, for instance, can either threaten human health directly, or they can produce indirect threats by degrading ecosystem services relevant to health. (See Figure 5, page 13.) These environmental threats may or may not lead to poor health

outcomes, depending on the vulnerability of the populations they affect.

What makes populations vulnerable? For one, a population must be at a critical threshold of resource consumption, below which there will be significant health impacts. The population must depend heavily on its local resource base and be unable to meet its needs by accessing a regional or global market. Finally, the population must lack the infrastructure, adaptive behaviors, governance, or access to international philanthropy that might otherwise protect it from the impacts of environmental degradation. Unfortunately, these qualities describe many of the populations of the developing world.

To avoid missing crucial connections, we must apply a new framework for analyzing the relationship between environmental change and health that includes not only the growing threats associated with accelerating environmental change, but also the presence or absence of insulating factors that can determine a population's vulnerability to these threats. Among the most worrisome relationships between environmental change and human health are those associated with infectious disease, food and nutrition, water scarcity and quality, air pollution, and greater vulnerability to natural disasters and forced migration.

Environmental Change and Infectious Disease

There is ample evidence that human disruption of ecological systems is changing the distribution of infectious disease.[1] Most studies show an increase in disease transmission as a result of altered environmental conditions, but there are also examples of such disruption decreasing transmission. (Draining wetlands where mosquitoes breed, for example, could eliminate a local source of malaria, although it could also reduce water quality and increase exposure to diarrhea and other waterborne diseases.)

Global land use and climate change drive new patterns of infectious disease exposure through a variety of mechanisms. These include changes to: the density or presence of disease-related organisms; exposure pathways (the way organisms, including humans, interact with each other); the genetics of pathogens; the life cycles of pathogens and vectors (typically insects such as mosquito, fleas, or ticks that transmit diseases by biting humans); and species composition within a community of organisms.

Infectious diseases that are transmitted by a vector or that have a non-human host or reservoir, such as malaria, dengue fever, schistosomiasis, and Chagas disease, are particularly sensitive to these types of changes.[2] Given that such diseases affect more than half the human population, alterations in their transmission can have significant impacts.[3]

Changes to Habitats and the Density of Disease-related Organisms

Collectively, changes in land use and climate are altering the biological composition, structure, and complexity of much of the global land surface. They change temperature, precipitation patterns, soil moisture, biogeochemical cycles, nutrient concentrations, surface-water chemistry, and exposure to sunlight. These parameters are often fundamental in defining the range and breeding habitat of numerous vectors, hosts, and pathogens. As they change, we can expect changes in the density or presence of these organisms.

Malaria offers a good case study because of its high death toll and its resistance to efforts at eradication and long-term prophylaxis. Each

A health worker checks standing water for mosquito larvae in a disturbed landscape in Dar es Salaam, Tanzania.

Table 1. Examples of Land Use Change and Increased Malaria Transmission

Land Use Change	Examples
Deforestation	In deforested areas of the Peruvian Amazon, biting rates of *Anopheles darlingi* are almost 300 times higher than in intact forest, controlling for differences in human density across varied landscapes. Similar associations have been observed in sub-Saharan Africa. In Asia, deforestation favors some vectors over others but frequently leads to increased transmission.
Dams	Microdams in northern Ethiopia increase the concentration of the local *Anopheles* vector and are associated with a sevenfold increase in malaria in nearby villages.
Irrigation projects	In India, irrigation projects in the 1990s improved breeding sites for *A. culcifacies* and led to endemic "irrigation" malaria among roughly 200 million people.
Agricultural development	In Trinidad in the 1940s, the development of cacao plantations caused a major malaria epidemic. Nurse trees shading the cacao provided ideal habitat for epiphytic bromeliads that, in turn, created excellent breeding sites for *A. bellator*, the principal local vector. The epidemic was not controlled until the nurse trees were reduced and plantation techniques changed. In Thailand, both cassava and sugarcane cultivation reduced the density of *A. dirus* but created widespread breeding grounds for *A. minimus*, with a resulting surge in malaria.
Wetland drainage	In Uganda, the drainage and cultivation of papyrus swamps caused higher ambient temperatures and more *A. gambiae* individuals per household than found in villages surrounding undisturbed swamps.

Source: See Endnote 5 for this section.

year, there are roughly 500 million cases of malaria and more than 1 million people (mostly children under the age of five) die from the disease, primarily in Africa.[4] Malaria is transmitted by a wide variety of location-specific mosquito species within the genus *Anopheles*. Many of the most pervasive types of land use change, such as deforestation, dams, and agricultural development, affect the density of different *Anopheles* vectors, leading to increased disease transmission.[5] (See Table 1.)

There is still active debate about how many more people will become infected by vector-borne diseases as a result of climate change; however, there is little doubt that climate change will alter the geographic distribution and seasonality of many of these diseases, including malaria.[6] In the highlands of East Africa, a warming trend from 1950 to 2002 coincided with increases in malaria incidence.[7] In India's Punjab region, malaria epidemics are strongly associated with precipitation and have

been shown to increase roughly fivefold during the year following an El Niño event when monsoons are particularly extreme.[8] Similar associations have been shown between malaria outbreaks and El Niño-related climate variability in Botswana.[9]

It is worrisome that the relationship between malaria and rising temperature does not appear to be linear. Just a half-degree centigrade increase in temperature can translate into a 30–100 percent increase in mosquito abundance as a biological threshold appears to be crossed, allowing successful breeding and survival of the vector.[10] In addition to malaria, clear effects of climate change have been established for cutaneous leishmaniasis, cholera, plague, and dengue fever.[11]

Schistosomiasis provides another example of the numerous ways that a common infectious disease may be sensitive to climate or land use changes. Schistosomiasis is caused by parasitic worms that spend part of their life cycle in

Environmental Change and Infectious Disease

Table 2. Examples of Land Use Change and Increased Schistosomiasis Incidence

Land Use Change	Example
Deforestation	In Cameroon, deforestation led to an upsurge in schistosomiasis as one type of freshwater snail (*Bulinus forskalii*) was displaced by another (*B. truncatus*) that was better suited to cleared habitats. *B. truncatus* was an effective host for *Schistosoma haematobium*, a primary cause of urinary tract schistosomiasis.
Dams	Construction of Egypt's Aswan dam in 1965 created extensive new habitat for *B. truncatus*. As a result, *S. haematobium* infection in Upper and Middle Egypt rose from about 6 percent before construction of the dam to nearly 20 percent in the 1980s. In Lower Egypt, intestinal schistosomiasis rose to an even greater extent.
Irrigation projects	In Kenya's Tana River region, the Hola irrigation project led to the introduction of snail vectors where they had never been before. Between 1956, when the project began, and 1966, the prevalence of urinary schistosomiasis in children in the region went from 0 to 70 percent. By 1982, it was 90 percent.
Overfishing	In Lake Malawi, evidence suggests that overfishing contributed to the recent surge of schistosomiasis around the Nankumba Peninsula. Studies found that as populations of snail-eating fish declined, the *B. globosus* snail proliferated in areas that used to be free of it. This relatively sudden surge in host density has been associated with a spike in schistosomiasis in an area historically free of the disease.
Livestock development	In China's Yunnan Province, an economic development project attempted to raise local incomes by giving villagers cows—which also happen to be a key reservoir of *S. japonicum* in the region. As the cows spread, they shed schistosome eggs into waterways, where the parasites could infect local snails. Disease rates surged, infecting up to 30 percent of some villages and correlating directly with cattle ownership.

Source: See Endnote 13 for this section.

freshwater snails and then leave the snails to penetrate the skin of people who enter contaminated water. The disease can damage the liver, lungs, intestines, and bladder and infects roughly 200 million people worldwide.[12]

A variety of land use changes have been associated with increased incidence of schistosomiasis, including deforestation, dams, irrigation projects, overfishing, and livestock development projects.[13] (See Table 2.) Deforestation, for example, changes the ecology of freshwater snail populations by increasing sunlight penetration, encouraging vegetative growth, and changing water levels and flow rates. Many snail species do not survive these changes, but those that do tend to be better hosts for the parasitic worms.[14]

The rapid proliferation of dams and irrigation projects worldwide has contributed

greatly to the surge in global schistosomiasis, as these projects generate new habitat for snails that are well adapted to the altered environments and to hosting schistosomes. In addition to schistosomiasis and malaria, other diseases associated with water projects include Rift Valley Fever, filariasis, leishmaniasis, dracunculosis, onchocerciasis, and Japanese encephalitis.[15] Although most large-scale water projects are required to undergo economic and environmental assessments, health impact assessments have generally been insufficient or non-existent.

Marine systems are also affected by global environmental change. Rising sea-surface temperatures and increased application and runoff of fertilizers that cause nutrient enrichment of waterways have resulted in a surge in harmful algal blooms.[16] Such blooms can lead to massive fish kills, shellfish poisonings, disease and

Global Environmental Change: The Threat to Human Health

death of marine mammals, and human illness and mortality. Worldwide, roughly 60,000 individual cases and clusters of human intoxication from algal blooms occur annually.[17] Health impacts range from acute neurotoxic disorders and death to subacute and chronic disease.

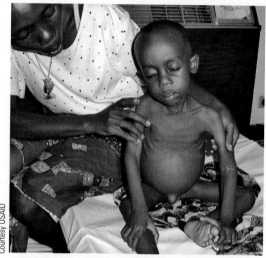

Courtesy USAID

In a refugee camp in Liberia, a mother comforts her son who is suffering from malnutrition and cholera.

Cholera outbreaks in Asia and South America have been associated with rising sea-surface temperatures, altered rainfall patterns, and nutrient loading from agricultural runoff. Copepods, a type of zooplankton, are a reservoir of *Vibrio cholerae*, the bacterium that causes cholera. High nutrient loads and warm water temperatures cause blooms of these zooplankton and can lead to the transformation of *V. cholerae* from a quiescent to a virulent form.[18]

Changes in Exposure Pathways

In addition to changing the density or presence of disease-related organisms, global change is also altering *routes* of infectious disease exposure. Some of these new exposure pathways have little to do with changes in the natural world—such as increases in trade and transportation that facilitate the rapid movement of disease-related organisms around the globe. However, many types of human-caused environmental change also lead to new exposure pathways.

Land use changes are often associated with the movement of non-immune workers into areas where they are exposed to infectious diseases with which they have little experience. In areas of the Amazon that are being cleared for agriculture and infrastructure development, farmers, road-building crews, and other workers often create forest edge that is ideal habitat for the mosquito species *A. darlingi*, driving the phenomenon known as "frontier malaria."[19] Similarly, in Côte d'Ivoire, the cultivation of coffee and cacao plantations creates excellent habitat for the tsetse fly, a transmitter of African sleeping sickness (trypanosomiasis), and non-immune agricultural workers rapidly become infected by this vector.[20]

A second exposure route results from direct human incursions into wildlife habitat. In Central Africa alone, some 1–3.4 million tons of bushmeat (meat from wild animal species) is harvested annually for food and other purposes.[21] Bushmeat hunters who reported direct contact with the blood or body fluid of non-human primates have contracted simian foamy virus, a retrovirus that is endemic in most Old World primates.[22] This finding provides further support for the already compelling hypothesis that the retrovirus causing HIV/AIDS was likely a mutated simian virus contracted through bushmeat hunting.[23]

Human infection with Ebola virus also likely had its origin in bushmeat hunting. Between 2001 and 2003, five human Ebola outbreaks were reported in the forest region between Gabon and the Republic of Congo. In each instance, the human outbreaks were preceded by outbreaks in wildlife, and researchers concluded that every case of human Ebola transmission was the result of handling infected wild animal carcasses.[24]

Bushmeat hunting itself appears to be driven by the need of growing populations to supplement their protein intake. In Ghana, for example, there are strong correlations between a shrinking local fish supply and increased bushmeat hunting over a 30-year period.[25] Heavy fishing by European Union ships in West African waters resulted in 20-fold increases in EU harvests in the region and in consequent reductions in fish available in local markets. Reduced access to this important source of dietary protein was identified as a critical driver of bushmeat hunting in Ghana's interior. Overfishing by heavily subsidized EU fleets, then, appears to be one of the driving forces behind increased bushmeat hunting and exposure to infectious disease, at least in Ghana and probably elsewhere in Africa.

Human incursions into wildlife habitat also stem from the expansion of settlement and farming, potentially increasing exposure to zoonotic disease (infectious diseases in animals that can be transmitted to humans). Research done around Kibale National Park in Uganda suggests that the transmission of pathogens between humans and non-human primates is related not to bushmeat hunting but to other factors including population growth, forest fragmentation, crop raiding, interaction with domesticated animals, and direct interaction of people and wildlife through farming, land clearing, scientific research, ecotourism, and conservation activities.[26]

Urbanization, an important land use trend and a central demographic trend of the early 21st century, also provides new pathways for infectious disease exposure. Humanity is believed to have become half-urban around 2008, and this share is projected to reach two-thirds by 2050.[27] Much of the rapid urbanization occurring today takes place in urban or periurban slums that lack quality housing and have few services for clean water provision, sewage disposal, or solid waste management.[28] In these settings, pools of contaminated water and piles of municipal waste and refuse that are capable of holding water (such as old tires) create excellent habitat for a variety of rodent hosts and arthropod vectors, particularly those that transmit dengue fever, malaria, filariasis, Chagas disease, plague, leptospirosis, and typhus.[29]

In addition, rural-to-urban migration brings people from different disease-endemic regions together in high density, providing a source for new infection as well as non-immune hosts. Migration can also erode social

capital, which creates an obstacle to building infrastructure to prevent disease transmission and can change disease-related behaviors as well.[30] Poor-quality housing that does not provide an effective barrier to mosquitoes, rodents, or fleas contributes further to the spread of vector-borne disease in slums. Finally, increased human population density and size both increase the likelihood of infectious disease becoming established in an urban population.[31]

Children in the Central African Republic watch as their father butchers bushmeat, including duikers (a local antelope) and a moustache monkey.

One example is dengue fever, which has spread rapidly out of Southeast Asia and the Pacific and become endemic throughout the tropics. With roughly 50 million cases in more than 100 countries each year, dengue is the most common mosquito-borne viral disease in the world.[32] It is transmitted by the bite of infected *Aedes* mosquitoes, which feed selectively on humans and often breed in human-made containers that collect rainwater, such as jugs, tires, metal drums, discarded plastic food containers, and other items. These characteristics make the insects well adapted to urban areas, and dengue is primarily a disease of urban communities.[33]

A final way in which global change can affect routes of exposure to infectious disease is by altering the fate or transport of disease pathogens. Warmer temperatures in Europe, for example, correlate with increased incidence of food poisoning. The relationship is strongest for the period one week prior to illness, is linear, and has been reproduced in multiple European cities. Presumably, warmer temperatures allow the pathogen (the strongest relationship was seen for *Salmonella enteritidis*) to survive and multiply in higher numbers.[34]

A city worker sprays a community garbage dump to control *Aedes aegypti* mosquitoes, the cause of dengue fever outbreaks in Dhaka, Bangladesh.

© 2001 Jean Sack/ICDDRB, courtesy Photoshare

Changes in land use can affect the fate and transport of pathogens as well. Agricultural and livestock practices lead to exposure to waterborne disease through direct contamination of water supplies. Protozoan parasites including *Cryptosporidium parvum* and *Giardia lamblia* are shed in the feces of domesticated livestock. During periods of heavy precipitation, they are washed into waterways and then into drinking water supplies. Sixty-four percent of farms studied in Pennsylvania had at least one cow infected with *Cryptosporidium*. On 44 percent of the farms, all bovine stool samples tested positive. On these farms, the cattle had full access to waterways that could be contaminated by their feces.[35]

This combination of land clearing and grazing ruminants with no buffer zones to protect waterways provides a widespread avenue for human infection. In Milwaukee, Wisconsin, in 1993, despite a new water filtra-

tion system, more than 400,000 people were estimated to show symptoms of cryptosporidiosis, and 54 died following a period of heavy rainfall and runoff.[36]

A study of all-cause waterborne disease outbreaks in the United States found a strong association with heavy precipitation, with two-thirds of the outbreaks following exceptionally rainy months.[37] The combination of more-extreme precipitation patterns associated with climate change and the continued expansion of animal husbandry may be a setup for growing numbers of waterborne disease outbreaks, particularly in parts of the world where there is little water filtration infrastructure to insulate populations from this risk.

Genetic Alterations

Other livestock management practices are affecting infectious disease occurrence by facilitating genetic alterations. The intensification of livestock management, with larger numbers of animals held in higher densities in closer proximity to other species, has allowed pathogens to proliferate and to develop genetic modifications more rapidly. These modifications can affect both pathogen infectiousness and virulence. Exposure of livestock to large quantities and varieties of antibiotics has driven the proliferation of antibiotic-resistant strains of *Campylobacter, Salmonella,* and *Escherichia coli*, all of which can cause serious human infections.[38] In Malaysia, high-density pig farming proved to be the critical factor in allowing Nipah virus to jump from bats to pigs and then to humans, ultimately causing over 100 fatalities.[39]

Smaller-scale, backyard livestock management systems can also lead to genetic exchange and alteration of pathogens. Influenza A viruses are highly infectious respiratory pathogens that infect a wide variety of species. Because swine are susceptible to both avian and human influenza viruses, they can serve as genetic "mixing vessels," leading to novel reassortment viruses that have the potential to cause pandemic influenza from strains to which human populations have little immunity.[40] It is increasingly clear that the H_1N_1 influenza strain that caused the 2009 pandemic—a strain that has been shown to contain DNA from avian, pig, and human influenza types—had its origins in this sort of genetic exchange between pigs, birds, and humans.

Close confinement of pigs and fowl, for example in Asian "wet markets" and Chinese pig-duck farms, fosters this type of genetic exchange.[41] The SARS epidemic is likely to have resulted from crowding of animals in live-animal markets in China. In this case, the species at the center of the epidemic were horseshoe bats and palm civet cats as amplifying hosts, with a possible role for raccoon dogs and Chinese ferret badgers as well. Most of the early cases of SARS were among people who worked with the sale or handling of these animals.[42] These practices, combined with the incursion of people into wildlife habitat, may help to explain why roughly 75 percent of emerging infectious diseases are zoonoses.[43]

Changes in Life Cycle of Vectors or Pathogens

Environmental change can directly alter the life cycle of disease-related organisms. In experiments in the western Kenya highlands, investigators showed that by reducing shading, deforestation raises the average temperature in homes by 1.8 degrees Celsius (°C) and in nearby aquatic habitats by 4.8–6.1 °C. Among *Anopheles* mosquitoes, these ambient temperature changes are associated with gonotrophic cycles (the interval between egg-laying episodes) that are nearly 60 percent shorter, a more rapid developmental period from larva to adult, and increased larval and adult survivorship. All of these, not surprisingly, increase the capacity of mosquitoes to cause malaria and the risk that exposed populations will be infected.[44]

Local deforestation has also been shown to increase the geographic range of less-abundant mosquitoes—in this case *A. arabiensis*—into higher altitudes. As a result of warmer ambient temperatures in deforested areas, *A. arabiensis* has a 49–55 percent higher adult life span and a reproductive rate about twice that in forested areas. It has been suggested that a combination of deforestation and climate change may facili-

tate the establishment of *A. arabiensis* as an important cause of malaria in the highlands of Kenya.[45]

This feedlot in the U.S. state of Iowa was eventually reconfigured to keep the cattle out of the stream.

Changing Species Composition

Complex changes in the types of organisms that make up whole ecological communities can have dramatic impacts on infectious disease exposure. In Belize, for example, the application of fertilizer to higher-elevation agricultural lands has been found to increase malaria exposure downstream. The influx of phosphorus and other nutrients causes short, sparse wetland vegetation to be replaced by denser, thicker vegetation dominated by cattails—a breeding habitat favored by females of the species *A. vestitipennis* over *A. albimanus*.[46] The result is a higher density of *A. vestitipennis*, a significantly more effective malaria vector.[47] Nor is Belize an isolated example. In a recent survey of 41 different pathogens on six continents, nutrient enrichment led to ecological changes that increased disease exposure 95 percent of the time.[48]

Lyme disease exposure in the northeastern United States also has a complex ecology. Lyme disease is caused by infection with the bacterium, *Borrelia burgdorferi*. In the northeastern United States, it is transmitted by the bite of the blacklegged tick. The most competent reservoir of Lyme disease is the white-footed mouse. The abundance of these mice is a good predictor of the number of infected ticks. Because acorns are this mouse's most important food source, the density of mice is strongly associated with the abundance of acorns in the prior fall. Not surprisingly, the abundance of infected ticks is also tightly associated with acorn abundance, although there is a two-year lag as a result of the long life cycle of the tick.[49]

But Lyme disease exposure depends on more than the number of acorns available. It also depends on the species composition of the entire mammalian community in northeastern forests. Because most other mammals are much less competent reservoirs of Lyme disease, the presence of more non-mouse mammals, on which ticks may feed, reduces the likelihood of a tick becoming infected.[50] This effect of biological diversity reducing disease transmission—known as the "dilution effect"—has been described in a variety of other diseases including West Nile virus encephalitis, hantavirus pulmonary syndrome, and bartonellosis.[51]

In a final example, human outbreaks of St. Louis encephalitis (SLE) have followed wet summers after dry springs. To cause mosquito infection rates sufficient to drive human epidemics, SLE must be amplified in avian hosts. In South Florida, drought conditions in the spring cause *Culex nigripalpus*—the mosquito vector—to restrict its activity to densely vegetated, wet, "hammock" habitats. Nesting wild birds also make use of these habitats in the spring, and it appears that drought drives the mosquitoes and birds into close contact. This forced contact provides for rapid amplification of the SLE virus in the infected birds. Subsequent wet conditions cause both birds and mosquitoes to disperse and favor breeding and feeding by *C. nigripalpus*. With a critical mass of wild birds already infected, newly hatched mosquitoes can be infected by feeding on birds that still carry live virus loads, thus maintaining the transmission cycle. The epidemic of SLE among human residents of Indian River County, Florida, in 1990 appeared to depend on this complex ecology of interactions among land cover, climate, wild birds, and mosquitoes.[52]

One theme emerging from research on such interactions is the complexity of relationships between land use, climate phenomenon, species diversity, and disease transmission. Directly stemming from this complexity is a second theme: the unpredictability of disease outcomes. Who would have predicted, based on logic alone, that a disease that stops oak trees from producing acorns might reduce human exposure to Lyme disease, or that more efficient use of fertilizers on mountain slopes of Belize might reduce malaria exposure hundreds of kilometers away?

A third emerging theme is the extent to which ecological disturbance appears to favor rather than diminish disease transmission. More often than not, disruption of historical land cover through deforestation, dams and irrigation, agricultural practices, and livestock management practices seems to boost the risk of disease exposure. Both nutrient enrichment and reductions in species diversity are additional causes of increased disease exposure in most systems that have been studied.

The reasons why degradation of ecological systems would favor increased disease transmission are not obvious. Some researchers believe that pathogens may have evolved with a preference for infecting generalist species, such as rats, crows, and sparrows. By doing so, they would have access to host species in a wide variety of ecological settings. Because ecological disturbance also tends to favor these generalist species (which are flexible in their habitat preferences), such an adaptation would explain the link between ecological disruption, increased prevalence of generalist species, and increased exposure to diseases caused by these pathogens.[53]

Environmental Change, Food, and Nutrition

Although the relationships between environmental change and infectious diseases are the best studied, they may not in fact be the most important health impacts of environmental change. Scarcities of food and water and greater vulnerability to natural disasters and forced migration could lead to higher human death rates and disease burdens than increased infectious disease exposure. At the same time, food and water scarcity, natural disasters, and displacement all contribute to infectious disease as a result of both weakened immunity and increased exposure.

The ecosystem service perhaps most essential to human health is food production. Adequate nutrition—not just a full complement of energy-storing calories, but also protein and essential vitamins, minerals, and other micronutrients—is vital to life. Yet today, an estimated 1.02 billion people—nearly a sixth of the global population—are undernourished, the highest number ever recorded.[1] (See Figure 7.) By some estimates, at least a third of the disease burden in poor countries is due to malnutrition, and roughly 16 percent of the global disease burden is attributable to childhood malnutrition.[2] Health impacts associated with nutritional shortfalls include impairments in cognitive development and learning, metabolic and endocrine functioning, reproductive health, prevention and fighting of infectious disease, and overall vigor.

As the human population grows by roughly 2.5 billion people by 2050, and as more prosperous people across the globe add more meat to their diets, world agricultural production will need to roughly double over the next 50

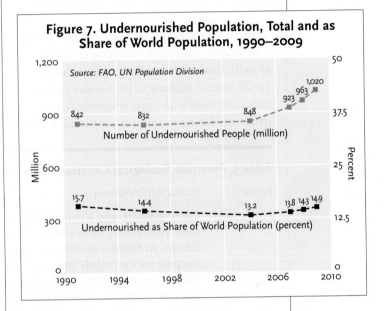

Figure 7. Undernourished Population, Total and as Share of World Population, 1990–2009

Source: FAO, UN Population Division

Number of Undernourished People (million)
842 832 848 923 963 1,020

Undernourished as Share of World Population (percent)
15.7 14.4 13.2 13.8 14.3 14.9

years to keep up with projected demand.[3] One of the central public health questions of this century is whether we can meet this demand or whether ecological constraints will stymie us.

This question must be answered at two scales, local and global. Because most of the chronically hungry people in the world are also among the over 1 billion people who live in absolute poverty, global food production is only partly relevant. Most of these people are too poor to access global food markets, and consequently depend on local production. For them, local ecological constraints can drive hunger, disease, and death, even while global food production exceeds demand.

In many parts of the world, rapidly growing populations are already encountering ecological constraints to local food production. Over the past 30 years, severe soil-nutrient depletion in 37 African countries has led to significant soil impoverishment and reduced output.[4] Similarly, water scarcity is necessitating grain imports in all but two of the 34 countries in Africa, Asia, and the Middle East that have annual per capita runoff levels below 1,700 cubic meters, a condition known as water stress.[5] With the number of people living in water-stressed countries in these regions projected to rise from 470 million to more than 3 billion by 2025, regional water scarcity is likely to affect local food production quite significantly.[6]

Increasing agricultural output at the global scale may be limited by ecological constraints as well. Some analysts are optimistic that a 10–20 percent increase in land under cultivation, combined with more widespread use of irrigation, fertilizer, and new crop strains, will allow a doubling of global output.[7] However, each of these elements may be ecologically constrained.[8] (See Table 3.)

Two other global trends are likely to affect food supplies. On the demand side, the acceleration of biofuels production has stimulated a new, non-food market for cereals that amounted to nearly 5 percent of global cereal production in 2009.[9] For the first time, hungry people are competing directly with motor vehicles for the same grain, a development that has potentially ominous consequences for the hungry poor.

On the supply side, climate change is certain to affect food production by altering biophysical conditions.[10] The Intergovernmental Panel on Climate Change projects with "high confidence" that many semi-arid areas (for example,

Table 3. Potential Ecological Constraints on Increased Global Food Production

Factor	Ecological Constraint
Arable land	Existing arable land already suffers degradation and outright destruction from soil erosion, salinization, desertification, and conversion to other uses, including rapid urbanization. As farmers increase production, approaches that may have been sustainable in the past are essentially "mining" soils unsustainably, resulting in dramatic net reductions in fertility. Tillage agriculture is estimated to cause erosion at rates that exceed soil formation by 1–2 orders of magnitude.
Irrigation water	Doubling agricultural output will require roughly an additional 2,000–3,000 cubic kilometers of irrigation water per year—the equivalent of over 110 Colorado Rivers and a more than tripling of current demand. Yet the three largest grain producers are mining aquifers faster than they can be recharged. In the North China Plain, where half of China's wheat is grown, water tables are falling by more than 1 meter per year. In India, 15 percent of grain production depends on water mined unsustainably from fossil aquifers, and blackouts are frequent in states where half of all electricity is used to pump water from as deep as 1 kilometer. In the United States, the water table below parts of Texas, Oklahoma, and Kansas has dropped more than 30 meters in the past century.
Fertilizer	Humans already release more nitrogen and phosphorus to terrestrial ecosystems than all natural systems combined. Doubling food production by 2050 will require increasing applications of both inputs by roughly 2.5 times, exacerbating already-serious impacts including eutrophication of marine ecosystems, biodiversity loss, groundwater and air pollution, and acidification of soils and fresh water.
Crop yields	In many large grain-producing areas, crop yields per hectare are approaching biological limits that leave little room for significant gains. In sub-Saharan Africa, where big yield gaps remain, the diversity of agro-climatic conditions makes disseminating high-yielding seeds particularly challenging. And while new crop strains may provide greater resistance to stress, there is little evidence that they provide significant gains in yield potential.

Source: See Endnote 8 for this section.

the Mediterranean basin, western United States, southern Africa, and northeast Brazil) will suffer a decrease in water resources.[11] Climate change is already causing rapid melting of glaciers that supply dry-season flow to many of the world's great rivers—including glaciers on the Tibetan plateau that supply water to more than a billion people downstream.[12]

Sea-level rise, weakened coastal barriers, and more-intense storms will lead to more coastal flooding and to inundation of coastal freshwater aquifers and fertile soils with salt water. Winter snowpack is expected to melt earlier in the year, disconnecting water supply from the height of the growing season in some areas. Warmer temperatures will also lead to greater evaporation from soils and plants and increase irrigation requirements for crops. All of these dynamics will further limit already-constrained access to fresh water for irrigation.

In addition, temperature rise has direct impacts on crop yields. Having been developed to maximize yields under current climate conditions, most cultivars now in use are grown at or near their upper limits of temperature for growth. A rule of thumb among crop ecologists is that a 1 °C rise in the minimum temperature during the growing season leads to a 10-percent reduction in yields of rice, wheat, or corn.[13] This was recently confirmed by a time-series analysis from 1979 to 2003 at the International Rice Research Institute.[14] Numerous modeling studies project similar sensitivities of the major grains to a 1 °C rise in temperature, with a yield change ranging from +3 percent to -17 percent depending on the region and crop.[15]

Such extreme temperature sensitivity could result in major reductions in crop yields in many of the most important food-producing regions, including the North China Plain, India's Gangetic Plain, and the U.S. Corn Belt.[16] While the net impact of climate change on global agricultural productivity is still debated, there is agreement that, at a mini-

Rice cultivation in Mali, with its demanding irrigation requirements, may not be sustainable in the future.

Courtesy USAID

mum, certain agricultural regions are likely to see significant overall reductions in food production, particularly in sub-Saharan Africa and South Asia—the regions where food insecurity has often been the highest.[17] Some researchers believe that climate change could reduce agricultural yields by up to 40 percent across much of the tropics.[18]

Climate change will create an additional obstacle to meeting global nutritional needs. There is strong evidence that grain grown at 550 parts per million of carbon dioxide (a level anticipated by 2050) contains 15–30 percent less protein, zinc, and iron than grain grown at today's levels. Already, some 3 billion people worldwide have zinc and iron deficiencies, and a large share of the more than 1 billion people suffering from chronic malnutrition have protein deficiencies.[19] The main source of these nutrients, particularly for women and children in the developing world, is grain because there is so little meat in their diets. Further reductions in access to protein and micronutrients is likely to cause a significant rise in the overall burden of disease. Thus, climate change is likely to affect not only the *quantity* of food available, but also the nutritional *quality* of food.

Other Health Outcomes

In addition to affecting exposure to infectious disease and access to adequate nutrition, human-caused environmental change adversely affects health through many other pathways. These include: water scarcity and unsafe water supplies, natural disasters, increased air pollution, and population displacement.

Water and Sanitation

One ecosystem service critical to human health is the provision of clean water. Each person needs roughly 50 liters of uncontaminated

Children collect water to take back to their village in the Volta region of Ghana.

fresh water per day to meet basic needs ranging from food preparation to drinking water, sanitation, and hygiene.[1] Inadequate access to drinking water, sanitation, and hygiene is estimated to cause 1.7 million deaths annually and the loss of at least 50 million healthy life years. Half of the urban population of Africa, Asia, and Latin America and the Caribbean suffers from one or more diseases associated with inadequate water and sanitation.[2]

Water is already scarce and getting scarcer. Humanity now uses roughly 40–50 percent of the available fresh water on the planet.[3] Rates of increase in water use relative to accessible supply from 1960 to the present have been nearly 20 percent per decade globally, with rates for individual continents ranging between 15 percent and more than 30 percent.

As with food, our ability to meet future water needs faces constraints on both the supply and demand sides. On the supply side, further intensification of agriculture and livestock will generate additional runoff of nutrients and wastes, causing groundwater contamination and pollution of freshwater systems.[4] Urbanization and the growth of manufacturing continue to drive both biological and chemical contamination. And climate change is already leading to physical changes that are likely to further reduce access to fresh water. On the demand side, population growth, continued economic development, and rapidly growing manufacturing and agriculture will continue to place additional demands on global freshwater supplies.

The health impacts of reduced access to clean fresh water depend on a variety of mediating factors. Wealthy populations, such as in

Israel, have developed highly efficient irrigation technologies, sanitation systems that require little water, and the economic capacity to import water in the form of grain (about 1,000 tons of water are used to grow 1 ton of grain). Poorer populations, however, are less capable of insulating themselves with technology and infrastructure and lack the purchasing power to replace locally constrained resources on the international market. Lacking such resources, they are vulnerable to local water scarcity just as they are vulnerable to local food scarcity. Such vulnerability varies by socioeconomic status as well as by gender and age; women, for example, suffer disproportionately as a result of water shortages.[5]

Natural Disasters

Increasing vulnerability to natural disasters is yet another area where changing environmental conditions may affect human health and wellbeing. Since 1980, the number of Category 5 (devastating) natural disasters worldwide has trended upward, with a record 40 such disasters registered in 2008.[6] (See Figure 8.) All but one of these events—which included Hurricane Gustav in the Atlantic Ocean; monsoonal floods in India, Bangladesh, and Nepal; and Typhoon Fengshen in the Philippines—were weather-related.[7]

Human vulnerability to disasters depends on such factors as where people live, the quality of their housing, disaster preparedness, the availability of early-warning systems, and environmental conditions. [8]As both the number of disaster events and vulnerabilities to them have increased, so too have the associated impacts.[9] Twice as many people were affected by natural disasters in the 1990s as in the 1980s.[10] Average annual losses for all disasters in the 1990s comprised 62,000 deaths, 200 million people affected, and $69 billion in economic losses.[12]

Data limitations make it difficult to evaluate the contribution that environmental change has played in increasing vulnerability to fires, floods, storms, tidal waves, landslides, and other natural disasters. Model simulations and empirical observations indicate that damage from the Indian Ocean tsunami of 2004 was

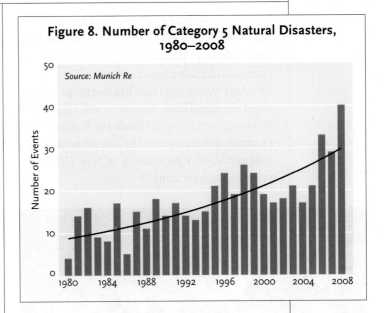

Figure 8. Number of Category 5 Natural Disasters, 1980–2008

Source: Munich Re

exacerbated by earlier destruction of coral reefs.[13] Additional studies have shown that areas where mangrove forests had been destroyed suffered disproportionate damage.[14]

Compounding these changes in land use and cover are current and anticipated changes resulting from climatic disruption. The IPCC has expressed "high confidence" that a warming of up to 2 °C above 1900–2000 levels (on the lower end of most projections for 2100) would increase the risk of extreme events including severe tropical cyclones, floods, droughts, heatwaves, and fires.[15] There is considerable uncertainty about the amount of sea-level rise this century, but recent estimates suggest between 0.8 and 2.0 meters, although higher levels are possible.[16] Higher seas will make coastal areas, where more than a third of the human population lives, particularly vulnerable.[17] The rapid destruction of coastal barriers such as mangrove forests, coral reefs, vegetated dunes, and wetlands, combined with sea-level rise and increasingly intense storms, represents a triple threat that is likely to cause significant morbidity, mortality, and population displacement.

Natural disasters can cause death or illness as a result of heat stress, acute injuries, or drowning. In addition, severe storms can result in pollution or biological contamination of water supplies, and air quality may suffer as a result of fires or of mildew in homes following flooding. Loss of homes and the resulting population displacement has numerous health impacts as well. (See page 29.) And we are only just beginning to understand the significant mental-health impacts of disasters. Survivors of Hurricane Katrina, for example, suffered twice the rate of mental illness as a similar population in New Orleans prior to the hurricane.[18]

Two women commiserate amid the rubble of buildings destroyed by severe flooding in Balochistan province, Pakistan.

Air Pollution

Extensive research documents the negative health impacts of both indoor and outdoor air pollution.[19] Most of this work falls into the realm of traditional environmental health, which addresses the local impacts of exposure to toxic pollutants. But in some regions, air pollution has become so extensive that it is literally blotting out the sun, altering regional weather patterns, affecting agriculture production, and accelerating glacial melting.[20]

Atmospheric brown clouds (ABCs), composed primarily of the combustion products of fossil fuels and biomass (including wood and dung used in household cooking stoves), cause an estimated 337,000 excess deaths from heart and respiratory disease annually in China and India. In addition to these direct health effects, ABCs prevent sunlight from reaching the Earth's surface, thereby reducing agricultural yields. ABCs are contributing to reductions in the Indian summer monsoon rainfall and to shifting rainfall patterns in eastern China.[21] Soot deposition from ABCs onto glaciers, particularly the Hindu Kush-Himalayan Tibetan glaciers and snowpacks, is further accelerating melting, with worrisome consequences for the water security of South and East Asia. All of these impacts of ABCs pose challenges to agricultural production and may explain in part the declining annual growth in harvests of rice, wheat, maize, and sorghum throughout Asia, from 3.5 percent during 1961–1984 to 1.3 percent during 1985–1998.[22]

Global environmental change is affecting air quality in other ways as well. Ground-level ozone is strongly associated with increased illness and death from cardiorespiratory disease.[23] The application of nitrogen-containing fertilizers to agricultural lands produces nitrous oxide (as does fossil fuel combustion), which is an important precursor to ozone formation. Of even greater concern, ground-level ozone formation rises with temperature, with a particularly strong association found at temperatures above 32 °C. Studies modeling climate change project increased concentrations of ground-level ozone with consequent increases in respiratory sickness and death as a result of higher temperatures.[24]

In addition, warmer temperatures and higher CO_2 concentrations are associated with longer pollen seasons and increased pollen production for many allergenic plants. For example, ragweed that is grown at the concentration of CO_2 anticipated for 2050 has roughly 60 percent more pollen than ragweed grown at current levels.[25] This trend will cause additional allergic respiratory disease, particularly asthma, which is already associated with a quarter-million deaths annually.[26]

Population Displacement

Population displacement and violent conflict could become common outcomes as large, vulnerable populations suffer amplified exposure to water scarcity, hunger, and natural disasters. Already in 2008, an estimated 42 million people worldwide were considered refugees or displaced persons, the majority of them in sub-Saharan Africa and Asia.[27]

The United Nations High Commissioner for Refugees estimates that between 250 million and 1 billion additional people will be displaced by climate change alone between now and 2050.[28] Sea-level rise and more-extreme storms will make some low-lying coastal areas and islands untenable for habitation. (Coastal areas less than 10 meters above sea level represent only 2 percent of the world's land area, yet they house 10 percent of the world's population.[29]) Similarly, altered precipitation patterns are likely to turn already-marginal agricultural lands into deserts that cannot support local populations. Local scarcities of food and water may drive populations out of resource-poor regions. These forces, working in concert, may lead hundreds of millions of people with few resources and many needs to seek new homes.[30]

Population displacement is associated with negative health outcomes for a variety of reasons. Non-immune populations migrating into disease-endemic areas are more susceptible to many infectious diseases.[31] Poor housing, sanitation, and waste management infrastructure, combined with unsafe drinking water and poor nutrition, can lead to epidemics of infectious disease, particularly diarrheal diseases, measles, and acute respiratory infections. Protein-energy malnutrition increases mortality from these communicable diseases and contributes independently to illness and death. Prevalence rates of acute malnutrition have reached up to 50 percent in refugee populations in Africa.[32]

In addition to malnutrition and communicable disease, displaced people suffer high levels of violence, sexual abuse, and mental illness. One study found symptoms and signs of post-traumatic stress disorder in 30 to 75 percent of resettled refugee children and adolescents.[33] Overall, crude mortality rates as high as 30 times the baseline are not unusual following an acute movement of refugees, with much of the mortality occurring in children under the age of five.[34]

Shanghai smog in 2005, from the Oriental Pearl Tower.

Added to the burden of suffering and disease associated with population displacement itself is the risk of violent conflict. Already, resource scarcity has played an important role in generating such conflict, and the prospect of significantly larger numbers of resource-constrained people seeking new homes in already-settled lands raises concern for greater conflict in the future.[35]

Adapting to the Health Impacts of Climate Change

International discussions about climate change, its impacts, and how best to reduce vulnerability cannot afford to ignore the linkages between climate change and human health. The disruption of our climate represents an accelerating destabilization of an already fundamentally unstable relationship between humanity and its natural resource base. Because climate change is a new and rapidly accelerating source of human-induced global environmental change, there is a special urgency to address it.

Climate change is a threat magnifier. It will magnify water scarcity in areas that already face unsustainable water use, and create new scarcities elsewhere. It will affect crop yields and generate obstacles to meeting global nutritional needs. It is also likely to cause more-frequent and severe natural disasters, alter the distribution of infectious diseases, and reduce the air quality across large parts of the globe. And—as a result of all of these effects and others—it is likely to cause large-scale population displacement and migration to a degree that humans have not before witnessed.

In a cruel irony, the suffering that will result from these impacts will occur mostly among the world's poorest populations—those who have made the least contribution to climate change. Many of these people live in countries that are already overwhelmed by existing public health challenges that stem from treatable conditions, such as malnutrition, diarrhea, acute respiratory infections, malaria, and other infectious diseases. Diverting limited personnel and resources away from these ongoing problems to address future threats from climate change could make things worse instead of better.

But the fact that climate change is a threat magnifier—and not, primarily, a source of entirely new public health challenges—may represent an opportunity as well as a challenge. If the international community accepts the moral imperative to help lower-income countries reduce their vulnerability to the health threats from climate change, it will also be helping those countries take strides toward addressing entrenched threats that have been a longstanding scourge to the health of their economies and people.

Approaches to Adaptation

Efforts to adapt to the health impacts of climate change must take three important characteristics into account:

- Many health impacts are likely to be large, affecting hundreds of millions, possibly even billions, of people;
- The magnitude, timing, and location of impacts are inherently unpredictable. The threats are not likely to be new, although their size may be unprecedented. Rather, they will be amplifications of existing health threats.
- The impacts will be experienced disproportionately by vulnerable populations in resource-constrained, low-income countries.

From these characteristics, several key concepts emerge. One is that there is a moral imperative for the wealthy world to assist lower-income countries with adaptation, given the size of the health threats, their preventability, and the disproportionate vulnerability of lower-income countries to them.

A second principle is the need to define "no-regrets" solutions. Despite improvements in climate change science, there will continue to be significant uncertainty about the location, timing, and magnitude of health impacts. At the same time, the impacts are most likely to be experienced by people living in countries with few resources to address already-existing public health threats. Given these realities, and the fact that climate change will magnify existing threats more than generate entirely new ones, adaptation strategies should be based on "upstream" interventions that will yield benefits regardless of the timing and location of specific climate-related events.

Examples of such "no-regrets" strategies are: improving public health infrastructure; developing more-diverse crop strains that are tolerant to a variety of different conditions (heat, drought, salt, etc); bolstering social capital and resilience, particularly in developing-country megacities; increasing storage capacity for fresh water by building reservoirs or recharging aquifers; creating early-warning systems and preparedness plans; and bolstering disease surveillance. We should design these types of activities with climate change in mind, but they will provide benefits independent of the precise impacts of climate change in a given setting.

Such an approach will help to avoid the danger of diverting limited resources in developing countries away from existing threats that are already responsible for large disease burdens. Many of these interventions may be undertaken within the context of ongoing foreign assistance. Indeed, there is a pressing need to contextualize the international conversation about the effectiveness of foreign aid and the achievement of the United Nations' Millennium Development Goals with an understanding of the impacts of climate change (and other types of global environmental change) and the need to reduce vulnerability to them. The challenge, then, is to focus development assistance so that it addresses existing threats independent of climate but simultaneously bolsters resilience to the amplification of these threats that we anticipate from climate change.

A third principle is the need to employ insurance strategies. Because the impacts of climate change in a specific location are unpre-

dictable, it would make sense to pool risk and develop insurance strategies whereby countries agree to help whichever populations absorb the greatest impacts. Before the victims of natural disasters, coastal flooding, droughts, crop failures, or acute water shortages have been defined, such insurance agreements could be put into effect.

In the aftermath of torrential flooding in Assam, India, people are reduced to foot travel on the remains of a washed-out road.

A fourth principle is the importance of surveillance. Because even the most sophisticated climate change models will be incapable of predicting biophysical changes in specific locations with great accuracy, surveillance becomes increasingly important. We know that conditions are likely to change, sometimes fairly rapidly. It will be important to gather and analyze information about field conditions across a variety of sectors. Surveillance of crop productivity, in-stream flow rates and water tables, food consumption and rates of malnutrition, and population movements will be as important to track as changing distributions of vector-borne disease, water-related disease, or other infectious diseases. These types of surveillance will be an important part of improving early warnings of climate impacts so that resources can be targeted to address emerging threats before they become humanitarian crises.

Adapting to the Health Impacts of Climate Change

A fifth principle is the importance of addressing demographics. Human population growth will increase vulnerability to many of the most worrisome health impacts of climate change. Food scarcity, water scarcity, vulnerability to natural disasters, and population displacement are all exacerbated by having growing populations relying on limited land and resources. One upstream intervention that should play a central role in both reducing greenhouse gas emissions and reducing vulnerability to health impacts of climate change is reducing the unmet need for family planning services.[1] (See Sidebar 1.)

Finally, there is an urgent need for more research to model the health impacts of climate change in specific locations, to evaluate approaches to reducing vulnerability, and to perform cost-effectiveness analyses on different adaptation approaches. There are many outstanding questions about how best to manage the relocation of millions of people or how to improve social capital and community action in developing-country megacities where 70 percent of the populations live in slums. There is a need to combine long-range weather forecasting with modeling of ecosystem services such as food and water generation and

Sidebar 1. Health and Environmental Co-Benefits of Family Planning

Currently, more than 200 million women worldwide do not have access to the family planning services they want or need, ranging from contraception to reproductive health counseling. Contraception allows couples and women to decide for themselves whether, when, and how often to give birth. Providing these services accomplishes three critical goals simultaneously: it reduces maternal and child mortality, it reduces vulnerability to many of the impacts of global environmental change by reducing pressure on limited natural resources, and it mitigates climate change by reducing greenhouse gas emissions.

Each year, some 80 million women worldwide become pregnant without intending to do so, resulting in high fertility rates in many parts of the world. This amounts to between one-third and one-half of all pregnancies and is roughly equal to the amount that the world population grows each year (79 million). Widespread adoption of family planning enables populations to maintain fertility rates close to or below two children per woman. After two or more decades of such low fertility, populations (and the world population as a whole) can stop growing and enter a period of improved stability.

Family planning increases the intervals between pregnancies, directly benefiting the health and survival prospects of mothers and their children. A child's survival is most likely when birth spacing is at least 36 to 59 months—an interval that can be achieved consistently only through contraception. Women at high risk for problem pregnancies can benefit in particular from access to family planning and the broader reproductive health care that should accompany it. By reducing the number of pregnancies and births, especially unplanned ones, the overall risk of death and poor health outcomes is reduced for each woman throughout her lifetime.

A gradual ending and reversal of human population growth (currently at 1.1 percent annually) is essential to long-term environmental sustainability. A smaller human footprint would ease pressure on natural resources—freshwater supplies, forests, fisheries, and biological diversity—while making it more feasible for global food production to feed the world while sustaining the planet. A smaller world population will also simplify the task of shrinking global greenhouse gas emissions in an equitable manner, especially later in the century as more widespread economic development results in greater equality in per capita emissions. Finally, slowing population growth is an adaptive strategy against many of the predicted impacts of climate change—food and water scarcity, natural disasters, and population displacement—all of which will be exacerbated by larger populations needing access to resources, secure homes, and productive lands.

Even in the absence of climate change, smaller, healthier populations would be a powerful component of more resilient societies. No other intervention would provide more benefits across the health and environmental sectors than providing global access to family planning services.

Source: See Endnote 1 for this section.

land-cover analysis to provide early warning for water scarcity, food scarcity, or epidemic disease. These types of research will need aggressive support to have an impact.

National Adaptation Planning

While the general principles above are critical to addressing the health impacts of climate change, specific policy recommendations must emerge from a careful analysis of local conditions. The most important truth about the health (and other) impacts of climate change is that both the threats and the vulnerabilities will vary tremendously by location. For this reason, it will be critical to perform national-level risk assessments that cut across disciplines and sectors. Such assessments must start with the best available projections of how local climate is likely to change, including changes in temperature, precipitation, sea level, and natural hazards. They should also include assumptions about demographic change, including population growth and migration, and about economic growth and infrastructure development.

Based on these projections, planners can model anticipated freshwater supplies, food production, changes in air quality, altered distribution of infectious disease, and future population displacement. National planners should also identify those sub-populations that are particularly vulnerable. These populations may be defined by ethnicity, gender, age, socioeconomic status, and geographic location. The threats in different places will be different. Some regions will highlight water scarcity or food shortages as critical, while others will identify coastal vulnerability or desertification and migration as the highest-priority threats. Without doing this type of rigorous risk assessment, it will be impossible to target limited resources to the highest-priority threats and the most vulnerable populations.

Once the highest-priority risks and the

Women at the Women's Skills Development Center in Pokhara, Nepal, receive family planning information.

most vulnerable populations have been identified, planners will be able to make specific policy recommendations. A country facing significant risks from water scarcity might emphasize the need to increase water storage through dams or recharging aquifers, or might recommend rapid adoption of more water-efficient irrigation or sanitation technology. A country confronting food shortages, and without the economic prospects to purchase food on international markets, might emphasize less-vulnerable forms of agriculture including the development of new drought- and heat-tolerant crop strains, more-efficient and widespread use of fertilizer, different approaches to soil management, or new crop types altogether. Coastal regions may need to invest in restoring natural coastal barriers, building infrastructure better capable of withstanding storm surge, developing early-warning systems for coastal flooding, or relocating populations entirely. In each location, the menu of interventions and policies that will be most effective at reducing vulnerability will be different.

Moving Forward in a Changing World

The need to act goes beyond mitigation of, and adaptation to, human-induced climate change. Accelerating changes to the planet's land surface and the functioning of its ecosystems are acting synergistically with climate change to generate emerging threats to human health at a scale that threatens the health and wellbeing of hundreds of millions—even billions—of people.

Collectively, these threats are likely to be the greatest public health challenge of the 21st century. Responding to them effectively will require new approaches to economic and human development, new technologies, and new research efforts, as well as new approaches to policy and decision making. Much of the human suffering likely to result from these trends is preventable—there is a tremendous amount that can be done.

Despite the increasing scale of environmental degradation and the growing risks of climate change and ecosystem disruption, there are many positive trends that should encourage us as we seek to slow the pace of environmental change and to lessen its toll on health. One critical factor is the size of the human population. Over the past four decades, the number of children born to each woman on average has fallen by nearly half, to only a fraction of a birth above the "replacement" fertility of slightly more than two children per woman. There is a strong possibility that human population growth will peak and reverse this century, although the world is still projected to gain well over 2 billion people before that occurs.[1]

There are other positive signs that we can reverse, or at least manage, some of the worst impacts of environmental change. Thanks to initiatives such as India's 150-million-stove program, improved cook stoves are becoming more widely distributed throughout the developing world, with tremendous implications for both reducing climate change and improving health, particularly among women and children. Meanwhile, farmers worldwide are turning to water-conserving technologies such as drip irrigation and to more-efficient "no-till" cultivation, a practice that saves both time and energy while producing similar yields to conventional farming.[2] Other encouraging trends include the rising proliferation of low-interest microfinance loans for the poor and self-employed (especially women), "bus rapid transit" and other improvements in urban transport and design, and new technologies that have enabled the costs of renewable energy to approach those of fossil fuels.[3]

In the health arena, inexpensive multimedia and mobile communications technologies are being applied in a concept called "m-health," a public health practice supported by cell phones, patient monitoring devices, and other wireless equipment that sends real-time patient data to health practitioners. As the explosion of mobile phone use continues in the developing world, telecommunications technologies are an important component of both economic and social development, including health-systems strengthening.

Innovations like these are characterized by the application of new thinking and evolving technology to an understanding of environmental and social constraints. More such innovation will be required on a massive scale to achieve true sustainable development and decouple current economic growth from future ecological collapse.

Research and Decision Making

From a research standpoint, we need to improve our understanding of the complex connections between environmental change and health. How do different types of human-caused change interact with local conditions to generate each of these emerging threats? What are the characteristics of populations that make them particularly vulnerable or resilient in the face of such threats? Which populations around the globe are at greatest risk for each type of threat?

To answer these questions, we need to do a much better job at integrating information across sectors and scientific disciplines. There is tremendous potential to advance our understanding by tapping large existing sets of environmental and social-science data and identifying relationships with human health. For example, a wealth of data is available from near-real-time environmental monitoring satellite platforms. These data could be analyzed with historical data on local and regional land use, climate, and socio-demographic conditions to help us identify relationships between health and the environment.

In addition to integration at the research level, we need better integration in the training of research scientists.[4] Researchers in health, natural, and social sciences need training across each other's disciplines so that they can work together collaboratively. Agencies and academic institutions should augment awards and promotion by developing criteria for scholarship in interdisciplinary pursuits, rather than the current incentives for reductionism in research endeavors. Government agencies like the U.S. National Science Foundation and the National Institutes of Health could work together to support more collaborative research efforts, including funding for post-doctoral fellowships that emphasize work across these disciplines.

While better integration and collaboration across disciplines is a critical step to improving our understanding of health-environment

relationships, we also need to fill several important data gaps. There is an astonishing lack of reliable, high-resolution, and geographically referenced data about population, health, and environmental conditions—or the host of other factors that determine vulnerability. We know little about the incidence or prevalence of most infectious diseases, water-related diseases, or different types of malnutrition at sub-national scales. We lack fine-scaled population data on key components of vulnerability: resource availability, socioeconomic status, quality of infrastructure, human behavior, or governance.

In West Bengal, India, a woman's stove burns methane from a village biogas project.

Nor do we have good data on some of the most basic and critical questions pertaining to environmental conditions that have very significant health consequences. Scientists disagree on how much additional arable land is available for cultivation or how much additional fresh water is available for sustainable use. Global rates of deforestation are not well established. We do not know how much arable land is becoming degraded by salinization, erosion, desertification, or nutrient loss. And we do not know how fast many of these processes are occurring or to what extent they are reversible. Without such basic information, we have little chance of making good decisions about policy or resource management.

But it would be misleading to imply that the only constraints are related to data. One of the major factors curtailing our understanding of the health impacts of global change is the subject's sheer complexity. While filling data gaps is key, it is also important to acknowledge that the complexity of some of these relationships will always make exact impacts of changing environmental conditions on human wellbeing difficult to quantify. In this context, it is critical to step-up efforts at surveillance so that we are able to detect changing patterns of infectious disease, malnutrition, heart and respiratory disease, morbidity from natural disasters, and environmental migration.

Deforested slopes erode above subsistence rice terraces on this hill in Madagascar. Once known for its lush growth, Madagascar is now known as the "Red Island" for the ruddy soil carried by its rivers into the Indian Ocean.

© 2005 Boris Pavlin, courtesy Photoshare

The emerging threats associated with changing environmental conditions also require a reorientation of policy and decision making. Public health practitioners cannot effectively protect public health without moving outside of the traditional health sector. Schools of public health and public health professionals need to expand their focus to include health impacts from global environmental change. "Strengthening public health infrastructure," a much repeated mantra, will not go far enough. Health professionals need to join their colleagues in sectors that have traditionally been considered unrelated to health to discuss the health impacts of different approaches to energy generation, food production, land use management, urban design, transportation, and water resource management. These topics should be integral components of public health research and training.

Decision makers in non-health sectors will also need to evaluate the impacts of their decisions through a public health lens. Decision making should be fully integrated, with coordination across agencies, and include policymakers involved in all aspects of economic development and societal wellbeing. Every development project—even relatively small and local ones—will have trade-offs and should require a Health Impact Assessment (HIA) in addition to requirements for environmental impact assessments. Treaty negotiations and large-scale policy decisions should include HIAs as well.

Sophisticated HIAs could provide answers to critical questions that would help us tailor our efforts to maximize health outcomes while addressing problems of global change. For example: How would varying approaches to reducing global CO_2 emissions affect human health, versus continuing with business as usual? How would widespread adoption of improved agricultural techniques or altered management of coastal zones affect health? How can ecosystems be managed to maximize their services while allowing for other uses?

One of the advantages of more widespread use of HIAs would be the identification of "co-benefits," whereby actions taken to address one problem can significantly improve public health at the same time. Replacing coal-fired power plants with solar or wind generation would help reduce carbon emissions and also significantly improve air quality and cardiorespiratory health.[5] Widespread adoption of cleaner-burning, more-efficient cook stoves would dramatically improve indoor air quality as well as reduce CO_2 and black carbon, a significant greenhouse gas that is also accelerating glacial melting. Designing urban areas to encourage walking and cycling would similarly reduce emissions while improving air quality and promoting exercise that has myriad direct health benefits.

A final important element is to bring these emerging public health threats to the attention of political, corporate, and other leaders around the world in order to encourage them to take strong action, both to reduce the pace of global environmental change and to help the populations at highest risk. Modeling the dynamics of each of the major public health threats associated with large-scale human-induced change and mapping out which populations are at greatest risk for each of these threats would provide leaders with the information they need to convince their constituencies of the importance of such actions and to target their resources in the most effective way possible.

Confronting Environmental Change, Confronting Vulnerability

It is impossible to project how much suffering will result from infectious disease exposure, constrained agricultural production, water scarcity, poor air quality, natural disasters, displacement, or civil strife without knowing the effectiveness of mitigating factors that protect populations from these threats. Will economic development increase the capacity of the world's poorest people to access international food markets? What degree of responsibility will the wealthy countries and international community take for helping the poor reduce their vulnerability? How rapidly will technology and infrastructure proliferate to make more efficient use of water, soil, and fertilizers;

produce energy more cleanly; break transmission cycles of infectious disease; or support a host of other interventions? To a large extent, our global society will decide how much suffering results from large-scale environmental change by the way it answers these questions.

Our inability to quantify current or projected health impacts resulting from altered environmental conditions should not be an excuse for complacency. Even without exact estimates, we have ample cause for concern. Numerous infectious diseases are changing their distribution, exposure pathways, virulence, and infectiousness in response to changes that we only partially understand—and new infectious diseases are emerging at an accelerating rate. Huge segments of the world's population already live without adequate access to food or water. Climate change represents a further destabilization of this already tenuous relationship between human populations and their resource base.

At present, all of the major types of human-caused environmental change—climate change, changes in land use and cover, and ecosystem service degradation—are accelerating. In concert, these trends are producing significant and growing vulnerabilities for large segments of the expanding human population. Many of these threats can be addressed with technology, infrastructure, policy, and economic development. However, with nearly half the world's population living on less than $2 per day, such development will require a level of international assistance and cooperation that is not currently evident.[6] To reduce avoidable human suffering, we must redouble our efforts to slow the pace of environmental change, humanely reduce the rate of population growth, and reduce the vulnerabilities of those in harm's way.

Endnotes

Expanding the Focus of Environmental Health

1. Figure 1 from United Nations Population Division, *World Population Prospects, 2008 Revision*, annual datasets on CD-ROM, forthcoming. Figure 2 recreated from Angus Maddison, *Contours of the World Economy: Essays in Macro-Economic History* (Oxford, U.K.: Oxford University Press, 2007).

2. P.M. Vitousek et al., "Human Appropriation of the Products of Photosynthesis, " *Bioscience*, vol. 36. no. 6 (1986), pp. 368–73.

3. P.M. Vitousek et al., "Human Domination of Earth's Ecosystems," *Science*, 25 July 1997, pp. 494–99.

4. J.A. Foley et al., "Global Consequences of Land Use," *Science*, 22 July 2005, pp. 570–74.

5. S.L. Postel, G.C. Daily, and P.R. Ehrlich, "Human Appropriation of Renewable Fresh Water," *Science*, I9 February 1996, pp. 785–88.

6. Foley et al., op. cit. note 4.

7. United Nations Food and Agriculture Organization (FAO), *Review of the State of World Marine Fishery Resources* (Rome: 2005).

8. Large dams refer to structures roughly the size of a four-story building or larger. World Commission on Dams, *Dams and Development: A New Framework for Decision-Making* (London: November 2000).

9. S.L. Pimm et al., "The Future of Biodiversity," *Science*, 21 July 1995, pp. 347–50.

10. Figure 3 from International Fertilizer Industry Association, electronic database, at www.fertilizer.org/ifa/ifadata/search, viewed 10 August 2009.

11. Vitousek et al., op. cit. note 2.

12. Figure 4 from the following sources: temperature data from J. Hansen et al., "Global Land-Ocean Temperature Index in .01 C, base period 1951–1980 (January–December)" (New York: Goddard Institute for Space Studies), at http://data.giss.nasa.gov/gistemp/tabledata/GLB.Ts+dSST.txt. Carbon dioxide is a Worldwatch calculation based on A. Neftel at al., "Historical CO2 Record from the Siple Station Ice Core" (Bern, Switzerland: Physics Institute, University of Bern, September 2004), at http://cdiac.ornl.gov/ftp/trends/co2/siple2.013; on D.M. Etheridge et al., "Historical CO2 record derived from a spline fit (20 year cutoff) of the Law Dome DE08 and DE08-2 ice cores,"

June 1998, at http://cdiac.ornl.gov/ftp/trends/co2/lawdome.smoothed.yr20; and on National Oceanic and Atmospheric Administration, data from 13 July 2009, available at ftp://ftp.cmdl.noaa.gov/ccg/co2/trends/co2_annmean_mlo.txt.

13. Maddison, op. cit. note 1.

14. Ibid.

15. United Nations Population Division, op. cit. note 1.

16. R. K. Plowright et al., "Causal Inference in Disease Ecology: Investigating Ecological Drivers of Disease Emergence," *Frontiers in Ecology and the Environment*, vol. 6, no. 8 (2008), pp. 420–29.

A New Health and Environment Framework

1. G.C. Daily, ed., *Nature's Services* (Washington, DC: Island Press, 1997); Millennium Ecosystem Assessment, *Ecosystems and Human Well-being: Synthesis* (Washington, DC: Island Press, 2005).

2. A. Balmford, W. Bond, and R. Cowling, "Trends in the State of Nature and Their Implications for Human Well-being," *Ecology Letters*, vol. 8, no. 11 (2005), pp. 1218–34; C. Corvalán, S. Hales, and A.J. McMichael, *Ecosystems and Human Well-being: Health Synthesis* (Geneva: Millennium Ecosystem Assessment and World Health Organization (WHO), 2005); C.D. Butler and W. Oluoch-Kosura, "Linking Future Ecosystem Services and Future Human Well-being," *Ecology and Society*, vol. 1, no. 1 (2006); WHO, "Human Health Under Threat from Ecosystem Degradation," electronic database, 2005, viewed 21 November 2008, at www.who.int/mediacentre/news/releases/2005/pr67/en/index.html.

3. L.E. Sieswerda et al., "Toward Measuring the Impact of Ecological Disintegrity on Human Health," *Epidemiology*, vol. 12, no. 1 (2001), pp. 28–32; M. Huynen, P. Martens, and R.S. De Groot, eds., "Linkages Between Biodiversity Loss and Human Health: A Global Indicator Analysis," *International Journal of Environmental Health Research*, vol. 14, no. 1 (2004), pp. 13–30.

4. Figure 5 is reprinted, with permission, from the *Annual Review of Environment and Resources*, vol. 34 (2009) by Annual Reviews, www.annualreviews.org.

5. A.T. Wolf, "Shared Waters: Conflict and Cooperation," *Annual Review of Environment and Resources*, vol. 32, no. 1 (2007), pp. 241–69.

6. R.F. Dasmann, "Toward A Biosphere Consciousness," in D. Worster, ed., *The Ends of the Earth* (New York: Cambridge University Press, 1988), pp. 277–88; K. Levy, G.C. Daily, and S.S. Myers, "Ecosystem Services and Human Health: A Conceptual Framework," in J.C. Ingram, C. Rumbaitis Del Rio, and F.A. DeClerck, eds., *Integrating Ecology and Poverty Alleviation and International Development Efforts: A Practical Guide* (New York: Springer, in press).

7. B.L. Turner et al., "A Framework for Vulnerability Analysis in Sustainability Science," *Proceedings of the National Academies of Sciences*, vol. 100, no. 14 (2003), pp. 8074–79.

8. A.K. Sen, *Poverty and Famines: An Essay on Entitlement and Deprivation* (Oxford, U.K. and New Delhi, India: Clarendon Press, 1981).

9. Figure 6 is reprinted, with permission, from the *Annual Review of Environment and Resources*, op. cit. note 4.

Environmental Change and Infectious Disease

1. J.A. Patz and U.E.C. Confalonieri, "Human Health: Ecosystem Regulation of Infectious Diseases," in R.M. Hassan, R. Scholes, and N. Ash, eds., *Ecosystems and Human Well-being: Current State and Trends. Findings of the Condition and Trends Working Group of the Millennium Ecosystem Assessment* (Washington, DC: Island Press; 2005), pp. 391–415.

2. J.N. Eisenberg et al., "Environmental Determinants of Infectious Disease: A Framework for Tracking Causal Links and Guiding Public Health Research," *Environmental Health Perspectives*, August 2007, pp. 1216–23; M.L. Wilson, "Ecology and Infectious Disease," in J.L Aron and J. Patz, eds., *Ecosystem Change and Public Health* (Baltimore: Johns Hopkins University Press, 2001) pp. 283–324.

3. S.M. Lemon et al., eds., *Vector-Borne Diseases: Understanding the Environmental, Human Health, and Ecological Connections* (Washington, DC: National Academies Press, 2008).

4. R.W. Snow et al., "The Global Distribution of Clinical Episodes of *Plasmodium falciparum* Malaria," *Nature*, 10 March 2005, pp. 214–17.

5. C.A. Guerra, R.W. Snow, and S.I. Hay, "A Global Assessment of Closed Forests, Deforestation and Malaria Risk, *Annals of Tropical Medicine & Parasitology*, April 2006, pp. 189–204; B. Singer and M.C. De Castro, "Enhancement and Suppression of Malaria in the Amazon," *American Journal of Tropical Medicine and Hygiene*, 1 January 2006, pp. 1–2; W.P. Tadei et al., "Ecologic Observations on Anopheline Vectors of Malaria in the Brazilian Amazon, *American Journal of Tropical Medicine and Hygiene*, August 1998, pp. 325–35. Table 1 derived from the following sources: Peru from A.Y. Vittor et al., "The Effect of Deforestation on the Human-Biting Rate of *Anopheles darlingi*, the Primary Vector of *Falciparum* Malaria in the Peruvian Amazon," *American Journal of Tropical Medicine and Hygiene*, January 2006, pp. 3–11; Africa from Guerra, Snow, and Hay, op. cit. this note, from A. Cohuet et al., "High Malaria Transmission Intensity Due to *Anopheles Funestus* (Diptera: Culicidae) in a Village of Savannah-Forest Transition Area in Cameroon," *Journal of Medical Entomology*, September 2004, pp. 901–05, from M. Coluzzi, "Heterogeneities of the Malaria Vectorial System in Tropical Africa and Their Significance in Malaria Epidemiology and Control," *Bulletin of the World Health Organization*, vol. 62 (1984), pp. 107–13, from M. Coluzzi, "Malaria and the Afrotropical Ecosystems: Impact of Man-made Environmental Changes," *Parassitologia*, August 1994, pp. 223–27, and from M. Coluzzi et al., "Chromosomal Differentiation and Adaptation to Human Environments in the *Anopheles gambiae* Complex," *Transactions of the Royal Society of Tropical Medicine and Hygiene*, vol. 73, no. 5 (1979), pp. 483–97; Asia from M. Coluzzi et al., "Chromosomal Differentiation…," op. cit. this note, from F.P. Amerasinghe and T.G. Ariyasena, "Larval Survey of Surface Water-Breeding Mosquitoes During Irrigation Development in the Mahaweli Project, Sri Lanka," *Journal of Medical Entomology*, September 1990, pp. 789–802, from N.L. Karla, "Forest Malaria Vectors in India: Ecological Characteristics and Epidemiological Implications," in V.P. Sharma and A.V. Kondrashin, eds., *Forest Malaria in Southeast Asia* (New Delhi: World Health Organization (WHO)/Medical Research Council, 1991), pp. 93–114, from F. Konradsen et al., *Malaria in Sri Lanka, Current Knowledge on Transmission and Control* (Battaramulla, Sri Lanka: International Water Management Institute, 1990), from D. Molyneux et al., "Ecosystem Disturbance, Biodiversity Loss, and Human Infectious Disease," in E. Chivian and A. Bernstein, eds., *Sustaining Life: How Human Health Depends on Biodiversity* (Oxford: Oxford University Press, 2008), pp. 287–323, from D. Taylor, "Seeing the Forests for More Than the Trees," *Environmental Health Perspectives*, November 1997, pp. 1186–91, and from J. Yasuoka and R. Levins, "Impact of Deforestation and Agricultural Development on Anopheline Ecology and Malaria Epidemiology," *American Journal of Tropical Medicine and Hygiene*, March 2007, pp. 450–60; Ethiopia from T.A. Ghebreyesus et al., "Incidence of Malaria Among Children Living Near Dams in Northern Ethiopia: Community Based Incidence Survey," *BMJ*, September 1999, pp. 663–66; India from V.P. Sharma, "Re-emergence of Malaria in India," *Indian Journal of Medical Research*, January 1996, pp. 26–45; Trinidad from W.G. Downs and C.S. Pittendrigh, "Bromeliad Malaria in Trinidad, British West Indies," *American Journal of Tropical Medicine*, vol. 26 (1946), pp. 47–66; Uganda from K.A. Lindblade et al., "Land Use Change Alters Malaria Transmission Parameters by Modifying Temperature in a Highland Area of Uganda," *Tropical Medicine & International Health*, April 2000, pp. 263–74; Thailand from Yasuoka and Levins, op. cit. this note.

6. K.D. Lafferty, "The Ecology of Climate Change and Infectious Diseases," *Ecology*, vol. 90, no. 4 (2009), pp. 888–900; K.D. Lafferty, "Calling for an Ecological Approach to Studying Climate Change and Infectious Diseases," *Ecology*, vol. 90, no. 4 (2009), pp. 932–33; R.S. Ostfeld, "Climate Change and the Distribution and Intensity of Infectious Diseases," *Ecology*, vol. 90, no. 4 (2009), pp. 903–05; R.S. Ostfeld, "The Ecology of Climate Change and Infectious Disease," *Ecology*, in press; D.J. Rogers and S.E. Randolph, "The Global Spread of Malaria in a Future, Warmer World," *Science*, 8 September 2000, pp. 1763–66.

7. M. Pascual et al., "Malaria Resurgence in the East African Highlands: Temperature Trends Revisited," *Proceedings of the National Academy of Sciences*, 11 April 2006, pp. 5829–34.

8. M. Bouma and H. Van der Kay, "The El Niño Southern Oscillation and the Historic Malaria Epidemics on the Indian Subcontinent and Sri Lanka: An Early Warning System for Future Epidemics? *Tropical Medicine & International Health*. vol. 1, no. 1 (1996), pp. 86–96.

9. M.C. Thomson et al., "Malaria Early Warnings Based on Seasonal Climate Forecasts from Multi-model Ensembles," *Nature*, 2 February 2006, pp. 576–79.

10. J. Patz et al., "Disease Emergence from Global Climate and Land Use Change," *Medical Clinics of North America*, November 2008, p. 18.

11. Pascual et al., op. cit. note 7; Patz et al., op. cit. note 10; Bouma and Van der Kay, op. cit. note 8; Thomson et al., op. cit. note 9; V. Southgate, H. Wijk, and C. Wright, "Schistosomiasis in Loum, Cameroun: *Schistosoma haematobium, S. intercalatum*, and Their Natural Hybrid," *Zeitschrift fur Parasitenkund*, vol. 49 (1976), pp. 149–59.

12. WHO, "Schistosomiasis," www.who.int/schistosomia sis/en, viewed 10 August 2009.

13. Table 2 derived from the following sources: Cameroon from Southgate, Wijk, and Wright, op. cit. note 11; Egypt from Molyneux et al., op. cit. note 5, from B.L. Cline et al., "1983 Nile Delta Schistosomiasis Survey: 48 Years After Scott," *American Journal of Tropical Medicine and Hygiene*, July 1989, pp. 56–62, from E.A. Malek, "Effect of Aswan High Dam on Prevalence of Schistosomiasis in Egypt," *Tropical and Geographical Medicine*, vol. 27, no. 4 (1975), pp. 359–64, and from Konradsen et al., op. cit. note 5; Kenya from C.M. Mutero, "Health Impact Assessment of Increased Irrigation in the Tana River Basin, Kenya," in International Water Management Institute, *The Changing Face of Irrigation in Kenya: Opportunities for Anticipating Change in Eastern and Southern Africa* (Colombo, Sri Lanka: 2002); Lake Malawi from J.R. Stauffer, Jr. and M.E. Arnegard, "Controlling Vectors and Hosts of Parasitic Diseases Using Fishes," *Bioscience*, vol. 47, no. 1 (1997), pp. 41–49; China from Z. Jiang et al., "Influence of Livestock Husbandry on Schistosomiasis Transmission in Mountainous Regions of Yunnan Province," *Southeast Asian Journal of Tropical Medicine and Public Health*, June 1997, pp. 291–95.

14. Molyneux et al., op. cit. note 5.

15. Patz and Confalonieri, op. cit. note 1; M.A. Appawu et al.," Lymphatic Filariasis in Ghana: Entomological Investigation of Transmission Dynamics and Intensity in Communities Served by Irrigation Systems in the Upper East Region of Ghana," *Tropical Medicine & International Health*, vol. 6, no. 7 (2001), pp. 511–16; M. Harb et al., "The Resurgence of Lymphatic Filariasis in the Nile Delta," *Bulletin of the World Health Organization*, vol. 71, no. 1 (1993), pp. 49–54; W. Jobin, *Dams and Disease: Ecological Design and Health Impacts of Large Dams, Canals, and Irrigation Systems* (London: E&FN Spon,

1999); D.F. Thompson et al., "Bancroftian Filariasis Distribution and Diurnal Temperature Differences in the Southern Nile Delta," *Emerging Infectious Diseases*, July-September 1996, pp. 234–35.

16. P. Hoagland et al., "The Economic Effects of Harmful Algal Blooms in the United States: Estimates, Assessment Issues, and Information Needs," *Estuaries*, vol. 25, no. 4b (2002), pp. 819–37.

17. F.M. Van Dolah, D. Roelke, and R.M. Greene, "Health and Ecological Impacts of Harmful Algal Blooms: Risk Assessment Needs," *Human & Ecological Risk Assessment*, vol. 7, no. 5 (2001), p. 1329.

18. R. Colwell and A. Huq, "Marine Ecosystems and Cholera," *Hydrobiologia*, vol. 460 (2001), pp. 141–45; R.R. Colwell, "Global Climate and Infectious Disease: The Cholera Paradigm," *Science*, 20 December 1996, pp. 2025–31; C. Ezzell, "It Came from the Deep," *Scientific American*, vol. 280, no. 6 (1999), p. 22; K. Koelle et al., "Refractory Periods and Climate Forcing in Cholera Dynamics," *Nature*, 4 August 2005, pp. 696–700.

19. Singer and De Castro, op. cit. note 5.

20. F. Fournet et al., "Impact of the Development of Agricultural Land on the Transmission of Sleeping Sickness in Daloa, Cote d'Ivoire," *Annals of Tropical Medicine & Parasitology*, March 2000, pp. 113–21.

21. J.E. Fa and C.A. Peres, "Game Vertebrate Extraction in African and Neotropical Forests: An Intercontinental Comparison," in J.D. Reynolds et al., eds., *Conservation of Exploited Species* (Cambridge: Cambridge University Press, 2001), pp. 203–41.

22. N.D. Wolfe et al., "Naturally Acquired Simian Retrovirus Infections in Central African Hunters," *The Lancet*, 20 March 2004, pp. 932–37.

23. B.H. Hahn et al., "AIDS as a Zoonosis: Scientific and Public Health Implications," *Science*, 28 January 2000, pp. 607–14.

24. P. Rouquet et al., "Wild Animal Mortality Monitoring and Human Ebola Outbreaks, Gabon and Republic of Congo, 2001–2003," *Emerging Infectious Diseases*, vol. 11, no. 2 (2005), pp. 283–90.

25. J.S. Brashares et al., "Bushmeat Hunting, Wildlife Declines, and Fish Supply in West Africa," *Science*, 12 November 2004, pp. 1180–83.

26. T.L. Goldberg, T.R. Gillespie, and I.B. Rwego, "Health and Disease in the People, Primates, and Domestic Animals of Kibale National Park: Implications for Conservation," in R. Wrangham and E. Ross, eds., *Science and Conservation in African Forests: The Benefits of Long-Term Research* (Cambridge, U.K.: Cambridge University Press, 2008).

27. United Nations Population Division, *World Population Prospects, 2008 Revision*, annual datasets on CD-ROM, forthcoming.

28. A. Norstrom, *Planning for Drinking Water and Sanitation in Peri-urban Areas* (Stockholm: Swedish Water House, 2007).

29. WHO, "Dengue and Dengue Hemorrhagic Fever," Fact Sheet No. 117 (Geneva: May 2008); A.I. Ko et al., "Urban

Endnotes

Epidemic of Severe Leptospirosis in Brazil," *The Lancet*, vol. 354, no. 9181 (1999), pp. 820–25; J.S. Mackenzie, D.J. Gubler, and L.R. Petersen, "Emerging Flaviviruses: The Spread and Resurgence of Japanese Encephalitis, West Nile and Dengue Viruses," *Nature Medicine*, December 2004, pp. S98–109.

30. J.N.S. Eisenberg et al., "Environmental Change and Infectious Disease: How New Roads Affect the Transmission of Diarrheal Pathogens in Rural Ecuador," *Proceedings of the National Academy of Sciences*, 19 December 2006, pp. 19460–65; G.C. Daily and P.R. Ehrlich, "Global Change and Human Susceptibility to Disease," *Annual Review of Energy and the Environment*, vol. 21 (1996), pp. 125–44.

31. R.M. May and R.M. Anderson, "Population Biology of Infectious Diseases: Part II," *Nature*, 9 August 1979, pp. 455–61.

32. WHO, op. cit. note 29; Norstrom, op. cit. note 28.

33. Mackenzie, Gubler, and Petersen, op. cit. note 29.

34. G. Bentham and I.H. Langford, "Climate Change and the Incidence of Food Poisoning in England and Wales," *International Journal of Biometeorology*, vol. 39, no. 2 (1995), pp. 81–86; R.S. Kovats et al., "The Effect of Temperature on Food Poisoning: A Time-series Analysis of Salmonellosis in Ten European Countries, *Epidemiology of Infection*, vol. 132, no. 3 (2004), p. 443; May and Anderson, op. cit. note 31.

35. T.K. Graczyk et al., "Environmental and Geographical Factors Contributing to Watershed Contamination with *Cryptosporidium parvum* Oocysts," *Environmental Research*, vol. 82, no. 3 (2000), pp. 263–71.

36. W.R. Mac Kenzie et al., "A Massive Outbreak in Milwaukee of Cryptosporidium Infection Transmitted Through the Public Water Supply," *New England Journal of Medicine*, 21 July 1994, pp. 161–67.

37. F.C. Curriero et al., "The Association Between Extreme Precipitation and Waterborne Disease Outbreaks in the United States, 1948–1994," *American Journal of Public Health*, August 2001, pp. 1194–99.

38. Patz and Confalonieri, op. cit. note 1.

39. Curriero et al., op. cit. note 37.

40. W. Ma, R.E. Kahn, and J.A. Richt, "The Pig as a Mixing Vessel for Influenza Viruses: Human and Veterinary Implications," *Journal of Molecular and Genetic Medicine*, vol. 3, no. 1 (2009), pp. 158–66.

41. Daily and Ehrlich, op. cit. note 30.

42. Z. Shi and Z. Hu , "A Review of Studies on Animal Reservoirs of the SARS Coronavirus," *Virus Research*, vol. 133, no. 1 (2008), pp. 74–87.

43. L.H. Taylor, S.M. Latham, and M.E Woolhouse, "Risk Factors for Human Disease Emergence," *Philosophical Transactions of the Royal Society B: Biological Sciences*, 29 July 2001, pp. 983–89.

44. Y.A. Afrane et al., "Effects of Microclimatic Changes Caused by Land Use and Land Cover on Duration of Gonotrophic Cycles of *Anopheles gambiae* (Diptera:

Culicidae) in Western Kenya Highlands," *Journal of Medical Entomology*, November 2005, pp. 974–80; Y.A. Afrane et al., "Effects of Microclimatic Changes Caused by Deforestation on the Survivorship and Reproductive Fitness of *Anopheles gambiae* in Western Kenya Highlands," *American Journal of Tropical Medicine and Hygiene*, May 2006, pp. 772–78.

45. Y.A. Afrane et al., "Life-table Analysis of *Anopheles arabiensis* in Western Kenya Highlands: Effects of Land Covers on Larval and Adult Survivorship," *American Journal of Tropical Medicine and Hygiene*, October 2007, pp. 660–66.

46. E. Rejmankova et al., "Freshwater Community Interactions and Malaria," in S.K. Collinge and C. Ray, eds., *Disease Ecology* (Oxford: Oxford University Press, 2006), p. 227.

47. J.P. Grieco et al., "Host Feeding Preferences of Anopheles Species Collected by Manual Aspiration, Mechanical Aspiration, and from a Vehicle-Mounted Trap in the Toledo District, Belize, Central America," *Journal of the American Mosquito Control Association*, vol. 18 (2002), pp. 307–15.

48. V.J. McKenzie and A.R. Townsend, "Parasitic and Infectious Disease Responses to Changing Global Nutrient Cycles," *EcoHealth*, vol. 4 (2007), pp. 384–96.

49. R.S. Ostfeld et al., "Climate, Deer, Rodents, and Acorns as Determinants of Variation in Lyme-Disease Risk," *PLoS Biology*, vol. 4, no. 6 (2006), p. e145.

50. K. LoGiudice et al., "The Ecology of Infectious Disease: Effects of Host Diversity and Community Composition on Lyme Disease Risk," *Proceedings of the National Academy of Sciences*, 21 January 2003, pp. 567–71.

51. G. Suzan et al., "Experimental Evidence for Reduced Rodent Diversity Causing Increased Hantavirus Prevalence," *PLoS ONE*, vol. 4, no. 5 (2009), p. e5461; F. Keesing, R.D. Holt, and R.S. Ostfeld, "Effects of Species Diversity on Disease Risk," *Ecology Letters*, vol. 9, no. 4 (2006), pp. 485–98; J.P. Swaddle and S.E. Calos, "Increased Avian Diversity Is Associated with Lower Incidence of Human West Nile Infection: Observation of the Dilution Effect," *PLoS ONE*, vol. 3 (2008), p. e2488; S. Telfer et al., "Disruption of a Host-parasite System Following the Introduction of an Exotic Host Species," *Parasitology*, vol. 130 (2005), pp. 661–68; B. Allan et al., "Ecological Correlates of Risk and Incidence of West Nile Virus in the United States," *Oecologia*, vol. 158, no. 4 (2009), pp. 699–708.

52. J. Shaman, J.F. Day, and M. Stieglitz, "St. Louis Encephalitis Virus in Wild Birds During the 1990 South Florida Epidemic: The Importance of Drought, Wetting Conditions, and the Emergence of *Culex Nigripalpus* (Diptera: Culicidae) to Arboviral Amplification and Transmission," *Journal of Medical Entomology*, July 2003, pp. 547–54.

53. F. Keesing and R.S. Ostfeld, "Disease Ecology," in J.C. Ingram, C. Rumbaitis Del Rio, and F.A. DeClerck, eds., *Integrating Ecology and Poverty Alleviation and International Development Efforts: A Practical Guide* (New York: Springer, in press).

Environmental Change, Food, and Nutrition

1.   Figure 7 from United Nations Food and Agriculture Organization (FAO), "Food Security Statistics," www.fao.org/economic/ess/food-security-statistics/en, viewed 6 August 2009, and from FAO, "1.02 Billion People Hungry: One Sixth of Humanity Undernourished, More Than Ever Before," press release (Rome: 20 June 2009). Population figures from United Nations Population Division, *World Population Prospects, 2008 Revision*, annual datasets on CD-ROM, forthcoming.

2.   F. Keesing and R.S. Ostfeld, "Disease Ecology," in J.C. Ingram, C. Rumbaitis Del Rio, and F.A. DeClerck, eds., *Integrating Ecology and Poverty Alleviation and International Development Efforts: A Practical Guide* (New York: Springer, in press); C.J.L. Murray and A.D. Lopez, "Global Mortality, Disability, and the Contribution of Risk Factors: Global Burden of Disease Study," *The Lancet*, vol. 349, no. 9063 (1997), pp. 1436–42.

3.   N. Alexandratos, "World Food and Agriculture: Outlook for the Medium and Longer Term," *Proceedings of the National Academy of Sciences*, 25 May 1999, pp. 5908–14.

4.   P.A. Sanchez, "Soil Fertility and Hunger in Africa," *Science*, 15 March 2002, p. 2019.

5.   S.L. Postel, "Water for Food Production: Will There Be Enough in 2025?" *Bioscience*, vol. 48, no. 8 (1998), pp. 629–37.

6.   Ibid.

7.   J. Bruinsma, *World Agriculture: Towards 2015/2030, An FAO Perspective* (London: FAO, 2003); C. Runge et al., *Ending Hunger in Our Lifetime* (Baltimore: Johns Hopkins University Press, 2003).

8.   Table 3 derived from the following sources: arable land from K.G. Cassman et al., "Meeting Cereal Demand While Protecting Natural Resources and Improving Environmental Quality," *Annual Review of Environment and Resources*, vol. 28, no. 1 (2003), pp. 315–58, and from A. Young, "Is There Really Spare Land? A Critique of Estimates of Available Cultivable Land in Developing Countries," *Environment, Development and Sustainability*, vol. 1 (1999), pp. 3–18; soil fertility from D.R. Montgomery, "Soil Erosion and Agricultural Sustainability," *Proceedings of the National Academy of Sciences*, 14 August 2007, pp. 13268–72; tillage from D.R. Montgomery, "Pay Dirt," *Scientific American*, July 2008, p. 76; irrigation demand from Postel, op. cit. note 5, and from M.W. Rosegrant, C. Ringler, and T. Zhu, "Water for Agriculture: Maintaining Food Security Under Growing Scarcity," *Annual Review of Environment and Resources*, vol. 34 (in press); North China Plain from J. Yardley, "Beneath Booming Cities, China's Future is Drying Up," *New York Times*," 28 September 2007; United States from L. Brown, "Could Food Shortages Bring Down Civilization?" *Scientific American*, May 2009, and from R.E. Kasperson and K. Dow, "Vulnerable Peoples and Places," in R. Norgaard and D. Rapport, eds., *Ecosystems and Human Well-being: Current State and Trends: Findings of the Condition and Trends Working Group of the Millennium Ecosystem Assessment* (Washington, DC: Island Press, 2005); nitrogen and phosphorus from P.M. Vitousek et al., "Human Domination of Earth's Ecosystems," *Science*, 25 July 1997, pp. 494–99; 2.5 times from D. Tilman, "Forecasting Agriculturally Driven Global Environmental Change," *Science*, 13 April 2001, pp. 281–84; crop yields per hectare from D.B. Lobell, K.G. Cassman, and C.B. Field, "Crop Yield Gaps: Their Importance, Magnitudes, and Causes," *Annual Review of Environment and Resources*, vol. 34 (2009), in press; new crop strains from Cassman et al., op. cit. this note.

9.   FAO, "Early Indications Hint at Smaller 2009 Cereal Crop," press release (Rome: 12 February 2009).

10.   Intergovernmental Panel on Climate Change (IPCC), *Summary for Policymakers of the Synthesis Report of the IPCC Fourth Assessment Report* (Valencia, Spain: 17 November 2007).

11.   IPCC, "Summary for Policymakers," in S. Solomon et al., eds., *Climate Change 2007: The Physical Science Basis Contribution of Working Group I to the Fourth Assessment Report of the Intergovernmental Panel on Climate Change* (Cambridge, UK: Cambridge University Press, 2007); IPCC, *Climate Change 2007: Impacts, Adaptation and Vulnerability. Contribution of Working Group 2* (New York: IPCC, 2007).

12.   IPCC, *Climate Change 2007…*, op. cit. note 11.

13.   L. Brown, *Plan B 3.0: Mobilizing to Save Civilization* (New York: W.W. Norton & Company, 2008).

14.   S. Peng et al., "Rice Yields Decline with Higher Night Temperature from Global Warming," *Proceedings of the National Academy of Sciences*, 6 July 2004, pp. 9971–75; D.B. Lobell et al., "Prioritizing Climate Change Adaptation Needs for Food Security in 2030," *Science*, 1 February 2008, pp. 607–10.

15.   Lobell et al., op. cit. note 14.

16.   Brown, op. cit. note 13.

17.   Lobell et al., op. cit. note 14; W.R. Cline, *Global Warming and Agriculture: Impact Estimates by Country* (Washington, DC: Center for Global Development and Peterson Institute for International Economics, 2007).

18.   D.S. Battisti and R.L. Naylor, "Historical Warnings of Future Food Insecurity with Unprecedented Seasonal Heat," *Science*, 9 January 2009, pp. 240–44.

19.   P. Högy and A. Fangmeier, "Effects of Elevated Atmospheric CO_2 on Grain Quality of Wheat, *Journal of Cereal Science*, vol. 48 (2008), pp. 580–91.

Other Health Outcomes

1.   P.H. Gleick, "Basic Water Requirements for Human Activities: Meeting Basic Needs, " *Water International*, vol. 21 (1996), pp. 83–92.

2.   C.J. Vorosmarty, C. Leveque, and C. Revenga, "Fresh Water," in F. Rijsberman, R. Costanza, and P. Jacobi, eds., *Ecosystems and Human Well-Being: Current State and Trends. Findings of the Condition and Trends Working Group of the Millennium Ecosystem Assessment* (Washington, DC: Island Press, 2005), pp. 165–207.

3.   S.L. Postel, G.C. Daily, and P.R. Ehrlich, "Human Appropriation of Renewable Fresh Water," *Science*, 9

Endnotes

February 1996, pp. 785–88; Vorosmarty, Leveque, and Revenga, op. cit. note 2.

4. D. Tilman, "Forecasting Agriculturally Driven Global Environmental Change," *Science*, 13 April 2001, pp. 281–84.

5. I. Ray, "Women, Water, and Development," *Annual Review of Environment and Resources*, vol. 32, no. 1 (2007), pp. 421–49.

6. Figure 8 from Munich Re, *Topics Geo: Natural Catastrophes 2008–Analyses, Assessments, Positions* (Munich: 2009).

7. Petra Löw, "Devastating Natural Disasters Continue Steady Rise," *Vital Signs Online* (Worldwatch Institute), 4 June 2009.

8. W.N. Adger et al., "Social-Ecological Resilience to Coastal Disasters," *Science*, 12 August 2005, pp. 1036–39.

9. R.E. Kasperson and K. Dow, "Vulnerable Peoples and Places," in R. Norgaard and D. Rapport eds., *Ecosystems and Human Well-being: Current State and Trends. Findings of the Condition and Trends Working Group of the Millennium Ecosystem Assessment* (Washington, DC: Island Press, 2005).

10. Ibid.

11. Ibid.

12. C.M. Kunkel, R.W. Hallberg, and M. Oppenheimer, "Coral Reefs Reduce Tsunami Impact in Model Simulations," *Geophysical Research Letters*, vol. 33 (2006), p. L23612; E. Marris, "Tsunami Damage Was Enhanced by Coral Theft," *Nature*, 25 August 2005, p. 1071.

13. F. Dahdouh-Guebas et al., "How Effective Were Mangroves as a Defence Against the Recent Tsunami?" *Current Biology*, vol. 15, no. 12 (2005), pp. R443–47; F. Danielsen et al., "The Asian Tsunami: A Protective Role for Coastal Vegetation," *Science*, 28 October 2005, p. 643.

14. W.T. Pfeffer, J.T. Harper, and S. O'Neel, "Kinematic Constraints on Glacier Contributions to 21st-century Sea-level Rise," *Science*, 5 September 2008, pp. 1340–43.

15. Ibid.

16. More than a third of the human population lives in coastal areas and small islands (within 100 kilometers of the shore and less than 50 meters above sea level). E.B. Barbier et al., "Coastal Ecosystem-based Management with Nonlinear Ecological Functions and Values," *Science*, 18 January 2008, pp. 321–23.

17. R.C. Kessler, "Mental Illness and Suicidality After Hurricane Katrina," *Bulletin of the World Health Organization*, vol. 84, no. 12 (2006), pp. 930–93.

18. K.R. Smith and M. Ezzati, "How Environmental Health Risks Change With Development: The Epidemiologic and Environmental Risk Transitions Revisited," *Annual Review of Environment and Resources*, vol. 30, no. 1 (2005), pp. 291–333.

19. V.M. Ramanathan et al., *Atmospheric Brown Clouds: Regional Assessment Report with Focus on Asia* (Nairobi: United Nations Environment Programme, 2008).

20. Ibid.; V. Ramanathan and G. Carmichael, "Global and Regional Climate Changes Due to Black Carbon," *Nature Geoscience*, vol. 1, no. 4 (2008), pp. 221–27.

21. Ramanathan et al., op. cit. note 19; Ramanathan and Carmichael, op. cit. note 20.

22. P. Eilers and B. Groot, "Effects of Ambient Particulate Matter and Ozone on Daily Mortality in Rotterdam, The Netherlands," *Archives of Environmental Health*, vol. 52, no. 6 (1997), p. 455.

23. M.L. Bell et al., "Climate Change, Ambient Ozone, and Health in 50 U.S. Cities," *Climatic Change*, vol. 82 (2007), pp. 61–76; K. Knowlton et al., "Assessing Ozone-Related Health Impacts Under a Changing Climate," *Environmental Health Perspectives*, vol. 112. no. 15 (2004), pp. 1557–63.

24. P. Wayne et al., "Production of Allergenic Pollen by Ragweed (*Ambrosia artemisiifolia L.*) Is Increased in CO2-enriched Atmospheres," *Annals of Allergy, Asthma and Immunology*, vol. 88 (2002), pp. 279–82.

25. K.M. Shea et al., "Climate Change and Allergic Disease," *Journal of Allergy and Clinical Immunology*, vol. 122 (2008), pp. 443–53.

26. Office of the United Nations High Commissioner for Refugees, "UNHCR Annual Report Shows 42 Million People Uprooted Worldwide," press release (Geneva: 16 June 2009).

27. L.C. Johnstone, "Planning for the Inevitable, The Humanitarian Consequences of Climate Change," presentation at "Linking Climate Change Negotiations and Disaster Risk Reduction," Copenhagen, Denmark, 12 November 2008.

28. G. McGranahan, D. Balk, and B. Anderson, "The Rising Tide: Assessing the Risks of Climate Change and Human Settlements in Low Elevation Coastal Zones," *Environment and Urbanization*, 1 April 2007, pp. 17–37.

29. J.D. Sachs, "Climate Change Refugees," *Scientific American*. June 2007, p. 43.

30. D.H. Molyneux, "Patterns of Change in Vector Borne Diseases," *Annals of Tropical Medicine & Parasitology*, vol. 91, no. 7 (1997), pp. 827–39.

31. M.J. Toole and R.J. Waldman, "Refugees and Displaced Persons. War, Hunger, and Public Health," *Journal of the American Medical Association*, 4 August 1993, pp. 600–05.

32. L.A. McCloskey and K. Southwick, "Psychosocial Problems in Refugee Children Exposed to War," *Pediatrics*, vol. 97, no. 3 (1996), p. 394.

33. M. Toole and R. Waldman, "The Public Health Aspects of Complex Emergencies and Refugee Situations," *Annual Review of Public Health*, vol. 18 (1997), pp. 283–312.

34. T. Homer-Dixon, *Environment, Scarcity, and Violence* (Princeton, NJ: Princeton University Press, 1999); Michael Renner, *The Anatomy of Resource Wars*, Worldwatch Paper 161 (Washington, DC: Worldwatch Institute, 2002).

Endnotes

Adapting to the Health Impacts of Climate Change

1. Sidebar 1 from the following sources: 200 million from S. Singh et al., *Adding It Up: The Benefits of Investing in Sexual and Reproductive Health Care* (New York: Alan Guttmacher Institute, 2003); 80 million from Alan Guttmacher Institute, *Sharing Responsibilities: Women, Society and Abortion Worldwide* (New York: 1999); a third to one-half from Singh et al., op. cit. this note; 79 million is a Worldwatch Institute calculation based on unpublished data from United Nations Population Division, personal communication of Robert Engelman with Thomas Buettner (note that the two numbers, on unintended pregnancies and annual additions to world population growth, are not comparable, since many unintended pregnancies end in abortion, and others displace pregnancies that would have later been intended); 36 to 59 months from S.O. Rutstein, "Effects of Preceding Birth Intervals on Neonatal, Infant and Under-Five Years Mortality and Nutritional Status in Developing Countries: Evidence from the Demographic and Health Surveys," *International Journal of Gynecology & Obstetrics*, vol. 89 (2005), pp. S7–24; risk of death and poor health from N. Prata et al., "Saving Maternal Lives in Resource-poor Settings: Facing Reality," *Health Policy*, vol. 89, no. 2 (2008), pp. 131–48; 1.1 percent from United Nations Population Division, *World Population Prospects: The 2008 Revision Population Database*, available at http://esa.un.org/unpp/, viewed 13 July 2009; P.A. Murtaugh and M.G. Schlax, "Reproduction and the Carbon Legacies of Individualism," *Global Environmental Change*, vol. 19 (2009), pp. 14–20; adaptive strategy from United Nations Framework Convention on Climate Change, "National Adaptation Programmes of Action," http://unfccc.int/cooperation_support/least_developed_countries_portal/submitted_napas/items/4585.php, viewed 11 April 2009.

Moving Forward in a Changing World

1. United Nations Population Division, *World Population Prospects: The 2008 Revision Population Database*, available at http://esa.un.org/unpp/, viewed 13 July 2009.

2. L. Raffensperger, "A Fresh Green for No-Till Farming," *Earth Trends* (World Resources Institute), 19 February 2008, at http://earthtrends.wri.org/updates/node/286.

3. Grameen Bank, "Microfinance in Action," www.grameenfoundation.org/what_we_do/microfinance_in_action, viewed 13 July 2009.

4. H. Eakin and A.L. Luers, "Assessing the Vulnerability of Social-Environmental Systems," *Annual Review of Environment and Resources*, vol. 31, no. 1 (2006), pp. 365–94.

5. J. Hess and S.S. Myers, "Climate Change and Human Health, in J.C. Ingram, C. Rumbaitis Del Rio, and F.A. DeClerck, eds., *Integrating Ecology and Poverty Alleviation and International Development Efforts: A Practical Guide* (New York: Springer, in press).

6. Population Reference Bureau, "World Population Data Sheet," fact sheet (Washington, DC: August 2005).

Index

Acorns, Lyme disease and, 22
adaptation, 5–6, 30–33
    international assistance for, 37
    "no-regrets" solutions, 30–31
Aedes mosquitoes, 19, 20
African sleeping sickness, 18
agricultural development
    area of land converted for, 9
    crop yields, 24, 25, 28
    malaria transmission and, 16
    movement of non-immune
        workers, 18
    "no-till" cultivation, 34
air pollution, 28, 36–37
algal blooms, 17–18
allergic respiratory disease, 28
Amazon basin, deforestation in, 16
Anopheles mosquitoes, 16, 18, 21
antibiotic resistant bacteria, 20
arable land, 24, 35
assistance, international, 8, 13, 37
Aswan Dam, 17
atmospheric brown clouds
        (ABCs), 28

Bartonellosis, 22
biological diversity, 22
birds, as pathogen hosts, 22
black carbon, 37
Borrelia burgdorferi, 21–22
Bulinus forskalii, 17
Bulinus truncatus, 17
bushmeat hunting, 18–19

Cacao plantations, 16, 18
Campylobacter, 20
carbon dioxide
    concentration in atmosphere, 10
    concentration, influence on
        nutrient content of foods, 25
cell phones, 34
Chagas disease, 15, 19
child deaths/mortality, 5, 10
cholera, 16, 18

climate change, *see also* environ-
        mental change
    call to action on, 5, 34
    characteristics of impacts, 15, 30
    confronting, 37
    disproportionate impact on
        poor, 30
    food production impacts, 24–25
    health impacts, adaptation for,
        30–33
    health impacts, complex rela-
        tionships with, 13, 14, 22
    health threats from, 7, 13, 14,
        15–22
    population displacement from,
        28–29
    synergistic effects of changes,
        11, 34, 37
coastal regions
    ecosystem services of, 12
    vulnerabilities of, 7, 25, 27, 29
collaborative research, 11
cooking stoves, 34, 35, 36–37
Copenhagen, Denmark, climate
        talks in, 6, 8
cows
    Cryptosporidium and, 20
    schistosomiasis and, 17
crop yields, 24, 25
    air pollution and, 28
Cryptosporidium, 20
Culex nigripalpus, 22
cultural factors, 12
cutaneous leishmaniasis, 16

Dams, 9
    malaria transmission and, 16
    schistosomiasis incidence and, 17
data gaps, 35–36
decision making for future changes,
        35–37
deforestation
    data gaps on, 35
    in Madagascar, 36
    malaria transmission and, 16

    mosquito life cycles and, 21
    in past 300 years, 9
    schistosomiasis incidence and, 17
dengue fever, 15, 16
    urbanization and, 19, 20
diarrheal diseases, 29
"dilution effect", 22
disease, *see* infectious disease
dracunculosis, 17
drip irrigation, 34

E. coli, antibiotic-resistant, 20
Ebola virus, 18
economic growth, 9, 10
ecosystem services
    clean water, 26–27
    complex relationships of, 12, 13
    degradation of, 12, 13, 14, 37
encephalitis
    Japanese, 17
    St. Louis (SLE), 22
environment
    health of, 9–11
    human modification of, 9–10
    new framework for, 12–14
environmental change, *see also* cli-
        mate change
    adaptation principles and
        strategies, 30–33
    call to action on, 5, 34
    characteristics of impacts, 30
    complexity of relationships, 13,
        14, 22, 36
    confronting, 37
    data gaps on, 35–36, 37
    food and nutrition and, 23–25
    framework for analysis, 14
    health threats from, 7, 11, 14,
        15–22
    infectious disease and, 15–22
    mitigation of, 5–6, 8
    momentum/time scale of, 11
    new approaches to, 34–37
    other impacts on health, 26–29

Index

research and decision making for, 35–37
environmental health, expanding focus of, 9–11
Escherichia coli, antibiotic-resistant strains, 20
Ethiopia, malaria in, 16
extinction of species, 10
extreme events and disasters, 27–28

Famines, 8, 13
fertilizer, 10, 24, 28
    malaria exposure and, 21
    runoff of, 17–18, 26
filariasis, 17, 19
fisheries
    declines in, 9
    overfishing, 17, 18–19
Florida, avian hosts in, 22
food and nutrition, 23–25
    constraints on increased food production, 24
    crop yields, 24, 25, 28
    malnutrition, 23, 25, 29
    nutrient cycles, 10
food poisoning, 20
forests, *see* deforestation
framework for environment and health, 12–14

GDP (gross world product), 9
generalist species, 22
genetic alterations, infectious disease and, 20–21
Ghana, bushmeat hunting in, 18–19
Giardia lamblia, 20
governance, as mediating factor, 12–13
grains
    crop yields and nutrient content, 24–25, 28
    use for biofuels, 24
greenhouse gases, 10
gross world product (GDP), 9
ground-level ozone, 28

H$_1$N$_1$ influenza, 21
habitat loss, 9–10
hantavirus pulmonary syndrome, 22
harmful algal blooms, 17–18
health, *see also* health impacts; health threats; infectious disease
    air pollution and, 28
    core "building blocks" for, 7, 11
    environmental, 9–11
    expanding focus for, 9–11

food and nutrition, 23–25
infectious disease, 15–22
mobile communications and ("m-health"), 34
natural disasters and, 27–28
new approaches to, 34–37
new framework for, 12–14
new specialties/concepts in, 11
population displacement and, 28–29
public health focus, 36–37
resource scarcity and, 13–14
water and sanitation and, 26–27
health impacts
    adaptation to, 30–33
    complexity of relationships, 13, 14, 22, 36
    differing vulnerabilities to, 7–8
    difficulty in quantifying, 37
    of ecosystem services deterioration, 12, 13
    governance and, 12–13
    Health Impact Assessments (HIAs), 36–37
    importance of addressing, 8, 36
    of malnutrition, 23, 25, 29
    planning for, 34–37
    risk assessments, 8
    time scales/delays in, 11
health threats, *see also* vulnerability
    from climate change, 7, 11, 13, 14
    synergistic effects of environmental changes, 11, 34, 37
HIV/AIDS virus, 18
human health, *see* health
human population, 9, 23, 34
    displacement/migration of, 19, 28–29
Hurricane Gustav, 27
Hurricane Katrina, 28

India
    cook stove program, 34, 35
    malaria incidence in, 16
infectious disease, 15–22, 37
    antibiotic resistance and, 20
    biological diversity and, 22
    cholera, 18
    "dilution effect", 22
    exposure pathways, 18–20, 37
    genetic alterations and, 20–21
    global prevalence of, 15
    habitats/density of disease-related organisms, 15–21, 37
    land use changes and, 16, 17, 18
    life cycle of vectors/pathogens, 21
    Lyme disease, 21–22
    malaria, 15–16

movement of non-immune persons and, 18, 29
schistosomiasis, 16–17
species composition changes, 21–22
temperature rise and, 16, 21
transmission decrease, 15
transmission increase, 15, 16–17, 22
unpredictability of outcomes, 22
urbanization and, 19, 20
zoonotic disease, 19, 21
influenza viruses, 20–21
infrastructure, 7, 12, 14, 18, 31
international assistance/ philanthropy, 8, 13, 37
iron deficiency, 25
irrigation projects
    malaria and, 16
    schistosomiasis and, 17
irrigation water/requirements, 24, 25, 34
Israel, water-use technologies in, 26–27

Japanese encephalitis, 17

Lake Malawi, 17
land use change, 11, 12, 18
    fate/transport of pathogens and, 19–20
    infectious disease patterns and, 15–21
    malaria and, 16
    schistosomiasis and, 17
leishmaniasis, 16, 17
leptospirosis, 19
life expectancy, 10
livestock development, 17, 20
Lyme disease, 21–22

"M-health", 34
Madagascar, deforestation in, 36
malaria, 15–16
    fertilizer use and, 21
    "frontier malaria", 18
    land use change and, 16, 18, 21
    temperature rise and, 16, 21
    urbanization and, 19
malnutrition, 23, 25, 29
marine systems, health of, 17–18
markets, access to, 12, 14, 23
measles, 29
mice, Lyme disease and, 22
migration
    infectious disease exposure and, 19
    population displacement, 28–29

Index

rural-to-urban, 19
Milwaukee, Wisconsin,
cryptosporidiosis in, 20
mitigation of environmental
change, 5–6, 8
mobile communications
technologies, 34
monsoons, 16, 27, 28
mosquitoes
Aedes, 19, 20
Anopheles, 16, 18, 21
Culex, 22
temperature rise and, 16
Myanmar, Typhoon Nargis and
(2008), 13

National Institutes of Health
(U.S.), 35
National Science Foundation
(U.S.), 35
natural disasters, 27–28
Nipah virus, 20
nitrogen cycle, 9
nitrogenous fertilizers, 10, 28
nitrous oxide, 28
"no-regrets" solutions, 30–31
"no-till" cultivation, 34
nutrient cycles, 10
nutrition, *see* food and nutrition

Ocean acidification, 10
onchocerciasis, 17
overfishing, health concerns associated with, 17, 18–19
ozone, ground-level, 28

Pigs, infectious diseases and,
20–21
plague, 16, 19
policy making, 36
pollen, 28
poor populations
dependence on local food production, 23
disproportionate impacts on,
27, 30
loans for, 34
need for international assistance, 8, 13, 30, 37
population displacement, 28–29
population growth, 9, 23, 26
possible peak and reversal of, 34
protein deficiency, 25, 29
protozoan parasites, 20
public health focus, 36–37

Rainfall/monsoon patterns, 28, 29
refugees, 28–29

research and decision making,
35–37
resource scarcity, health outcomes
and, 13–14, 29, 37
respiratory diseases/infections,
28, 29
retroviruses, 18
rice yields, 25, 28
Rift Valley Fever, 17
risk assessments, 8
runoff of fertilizer/nutrients,
17–18, 26

St. Louis encephalitis (SLE), 22
Salmonella, antibiotic-resistant
strains, 20
Salmonella enteritidis, 20
sanitation, health impacts of, 26–27
SARS epidemic, 21
Schistosoma haematobium, 17
schistosomiasis, 15, 16–17
sea-level rise
coastal vulnerability and, 25,
27, 29
estimates for this century, 27
simian foamy virus, 18
snails, schistosomiasis and, 17
soil-nutrient depletion, 23–24
soot (black carbon), 28, 37
species composition, changes in,
21–22
species extinction, 10
surveillance, need for, 31, 36
swine, infectious diseases and,
20–21
synergistic effects of environmental
and health changes, 11,
34, 37

Temperature, global surface, 10
temperature rise
algal blooms and, 17–18
cholera and, 18
disease pathogen fate/transport
and, 19–20
extreme events increased by, 27
food production and, 25
ground-level ozone and, 28
malaria and, 16, 21
Tibetan plateau, water supply from,
7, 28
ticks, Lyme disease and, 21–22
trypanosomiasis, 18
tsetse fly, 18
tsunami, Indian Ocean (2004), 27
Typhoon Fenshen, 27
Typhoon Nargis, 13
typhus, 19

Uganda
wetland drainage and malaria
in, 16
zoonotic disease research in, 19
United Nations' Millennium
Development Goals, 8
urban transport, 34
urbanization
infectious disease exposure and,
19, 20
water contamination and, 26

Vector-borne diseases, 16–22
Vibrio cholerae, 18
violent conflicts, 28–29
viruses, 18, 20–21, 22
vulnerability, 7–8, 12, 14
of coastal regions, 7, 25, 27, 29
confronting, 37
cultural behaviors for
reducing, 12
data gaps on, 35
to natural disasters, 27–28

Water
conservation technologies, 34
contamination, 26
dams, impacts of, 9, 16, 17
health impacts, 26–27
irrigation, 24, 25, 34
resources, decrease in, 24–25, 27
supply, threats to, 7, 20, 26
water projects, infectious disease
and, 16, 17
waterborne illnesses, 20
West Nile virus encephalitis, 22
wetland drainage, 16
white-footed mouse, 22
wildlife habitat, movement of
humans into, 18–19

Zinc deficiency, 25
zoonotic disease, 19, 21

Other Worldwatch Reports

Worldwatch Reports provide in-depth, quantitative, and qualitative analysis of the major issues affecting prospects for a sustainable society. The Reports are written by members of the Worldwatch Institute research staff or outside specialists and are reviewed by experts unaffiliated with Worldwatch. They are used as concise and authoritative references by governments, nongovernmental organizations, and educational institutions worldwide.

On Climate Change, Energy, and Materials

180: Red, White, and Green: Transforming U.S. Biofuels, 2009
179: Mitigating Climate Change Through Food and Land Use, 2009
178: Low-Carbon Energy: A Roadmap, 2008
175: Powering China's Development: the Role of Renewable Energy, 2007
169: Mainstreaming Renewable Energy in the 21st Century, 2004
160: Reading the Weathervane: Climate Policy From Rio to Johannesburg, 2002
157: Hydrogen Futures: Toward a Sustainable Energy System, 2001
151: Micropower: The Next Electrical Era, 2000
149: Paper Cuts: Recovering the Paper Landscape, 1999
144: Mind Over Matter: Recasting the Role of Materials in Our Lives, 1998
138: Rising Sun, Gathering Winds: Policies To Stabilize the Climate and Strengthen Economies, 1997

On Ecological and Human Health

174: Oceans in Peril: Protecting Marine Biodiversity, 2007
165: Winged Messengers: The Decline of Birds, 2003
153: Why Poison Ourselves: A Precautionary Approach to Synthetic Chemicals, 2000
148: Nature's Cornucopia: Our Stakes in Plant Diversity, 1999
145: Safeguarding the Health of Oceans, 1999
142: Rocking the Boat: Conserving Fisheries and Protecting Jobs, 1998
141: Losing Strands in the Web of Life: Vertebrate Declines and the Conservation of Biological Diversity, 1998
140: Taking a Stand: Cultivating a New Relationship With the World's Forests, 1998

On Economics, Institutions, and Security

177: Green Jobs: Working for People and the Environment, 2008
173: Beyond Disasters: Creating Opportunities for Peace, 2007
168: Venture Capitalism for a Tropical Forest: Cocoa in the Mata Atlântica, 2003
167: Sustainable Development for the Second World: Ukraine and the Nations in Transition, 2003
166: Purchasing Power: Harnessing Institutional Procurement for People and the Planet, 2003
164: Invoking the Spirit: Religion and Spirituality in the Quest for a Sustainable World, 2002
162: The Anatomy of Resource Wars, 2002
159: Traveling Light: New Paths for International Tourism, 2001
158: Unnatural Disasters, 2001

On Food, Water, Population, and Urbanization

176: Farming Fish for the Future, 2008
172: Catch of the Day: Choosing Seafood for Healthier Oceans, 2007
171: Happier Meals: Rethinking the Global Meat Industry, 2005
170: Liquid Assets: The Critical Need to Safeguard Freshwater Ecosytems, 2005
163: Home Grown: The Case for Local Food in a Global Market, 2002
161: Correcting Gender Myopia: Gender Equity, Women's Welfare, and the Environment, 2002
156: City Limits: Putting the Brakes on Sprawl, 2001
154: Deep Trouble: The Hidden Threat of Groundwater Pollution, 2000
150: Underfed and Overfed: The Global Epidemic of Malnutrition, 2000
147: Reinventing Cities for People and the Planet, 1999

To see our complete list of Reports, visit www.worldwatch.org/taxonomy/term/40